Obsession
John Wood and the Creation of Georgian Bath

The Building of Bath Museum

Contents

Detail showing John Wood from
The Four Bath Worthies [Cat. No.16]

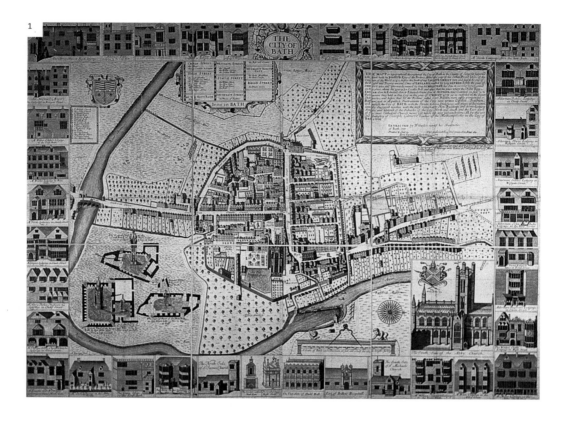

1 *The City of Bath*
Joseph Gilmore
1694
Engraving
760 x 960mm
Bath Preservation Trust
26G

This map, drawn by a mathematician from Bristol, clearly shows the size of Bath in the final years of the 17th century. Still encased by its medieval wall, the city was a collection of churches, lodging houses and baths, many of which are illustrated around the sides of the map.

The face of this relatively small walled city was changed forever by the imagination and influence of John Wood the Elder.

M Forsyth, Bath, *Pevsner Architectural Guides*, Yale University Press, 2004. W Ison, *The Georgian Buildings of Bath 1700-1830*, 1948 (second edition 1980). J Lees-Milne & D Ford, *Images of Bath*, St Helena Press, 1982, Cat. 1000.

Cathryn Spence

Preface

2004 marks the tercentenary of John Wood's birth and the 250-year anniversary of his death. This publication and the associated exhibition, *Obsession: John Wood and the Creation of Georgian Bath* (7 September 2004-6 February 2005), held at The Building of Bath Museum are the result of a year-long investigation into the life and work of Bath's most significant and pivotal architect. I initially had the idea to celebrate this landmark in Bath's history back in 2001 when I first arrived as curator at the museum. From the outset I was fortunate to have the support of Dr Timothy Mowl who kindly acted as consultant curator for the exhibition and as editor of this catalogue.

The Bath that John Wood knew when he was growing up was extremely provincial and unsophisticated. Curious stories of naked bathing, the dumping of dead sheep in the King's Bath and leprous pigs dominate. Its vernacular architecture, recorded in Joseph Gilmore's 1694 map, was only just beginning to emerge beyond the restrictive medieval wall system [Cat. No. 1]. John Wood's modern and ambitious plan for Bath saw the city spread out and engulf the once rural Barton Fields and Lansdown, resulting in a truly majestic city that still leaves its visitors in awe.

We are indebted to the Medlock Trust who, through their generous grant, made this publication possible. It was important to us that the research undertaken for the exhibition had its own lasting legacy in the form of a catalogue. The catalogue is complemented by three new essays that bring further thoughts to the intriguing debate on John Wood's motivations, his relationships and his lasting contribution to British architecture. The catalogue was printed by APB Colour Print. The exhibition itself was supported by a grant from the Heritage Lottery Fund. This enabled the museum to employ Amy Frost as the exhibition researcher and curator, Howard Batho as the exhibition organiser, Robert Shaw from Northbank as the designer, Joseph Beales as the exhibition build co-ordinator and myself as the project leader.

Many other individuals and local companies supported this project and a full list of acknowledgements can be found on page 112. It is only through everyone's enthusiastic and often unflinching support of this project that a celebration of 'the Effect of [John Wood's] great genius' was made possible.[1]

1   Obituary, *Bath Chronicle*, 15 July 1754

Dan Cruickshank

Foreword

A study of the life and work of John Wood opens a window into the amazing and little-known world of 18th century mysticism and speculative history. Once you understand Wood's intentions – and confront the breadth of his imagination – you will never see Georgian Bath in the same way again; indeed a deeper understanding of Wood's work gives new meaning to much 18th century architecture.

Wood is himself something of a mystery. Born in Bath in 1704, the son of a humble local builder, at the age of about 21 he went to London and then to Yorkshire to pursue his architectural career. The prodigy returned to Bath in 1727 – with an extraordinary vision. He wanted to remake it as a great Classical city inspired by Bath's own Roman past. When this initial, somewhat conventional, vision failed Wood started on a far more curious and fantastic journey. Inspired by his researches into the ancient and fabled history of King Bladud's Bath of pre-Roman times, by an examination of the ancient stone circles of Stonehenge and Stanton Drew, through his possible connections with Freemasonry and by immersing himself in the then emerging history of Britain's ancient Druids, Wood came up with another vision for Bath. And this is the vision he built.

The creation of Wood's Bath is a fantastic story that speaks of an intriguing search for national identity and pride, for essential spiritual values, for divine and immutable laws that lead to architectural beauty, and for a vibrant contemporary architecture based on an inspired interpretation of history.

Whether Wood was right or wrong (and few would now agree with his interpretation of history!) is beside the point. What the annual droves of admiring visitors to Bath prove is that, whatever his intentions, Wood succeeded in the creation of buildings and urban spaces of great and enduring beauty. Their proportions, forms and details may not have had the origin Wood imagined but they work – and with a vengeance.

This catalogue tells the story of the many-faceted John Wood, the story of his vision for Bath and for a British architecture, and of the portions of Bath he created. It is a story that continues to amaze and inspire.

John Wood and Charles Bridgeman: Bath as a garden city
Timothy Mowl

Fig. 1

It was while I was travelling extensively in the county for my book on the historic gardens of Wiltshire that the Bridgeman connections with Bath, just over the county border, came to me;[1] not directly, but during my research into one of John Wood the Elder's best villas, Belcomb Brook on the outskirts of Bradford-on-Avon, his demonstration of the Ionic order. Belcomb's garden [fig. 1] was one I knew well and had always taken as a small, but very carefully considered, example of a 'Rococo' Arcadia, with its serpentine Pool, contorted Grotto, Gothick Cottage, and that 'Model of the Octostyle Monopterick Temple of Delphos', which Wood had so desperately wanted to build himself, but which Francis Yerbury, the owner, gave to a 'Working Mason', who probably tendered much cheaper.[2]

Appearances are, however, deceptive. One of my MA Garden History students, Charlotte Gale, put me onto a 1777 map of the villa and its grounds in the Bodleian Library by James Sartain that told a very different story[3] [fig. 2]. Successive owners may have groomed the garden at Belcomb Brook into its Arcadian good looks, but originally it was a strictly formal affair, apart from the classical Temple, with a narrow, geometrical canal squashed up against the public road acting as a reservoir for the Yerbury clothiers' industrial complex strung out along the road. Behind the house, cut into the steep slope, there was a little courtyard with pavilions at each corner and columns between them. On the axial line from this delightful feature was a hedged vegetable garden, then another small pavilion in a triangle of topiary hedges.

Fig. 2

1   Timothy Mowl, *Historic Gardens of Wiltshire* (Stroud, 2004).
2   John Wood, *An Essay Towards a Description of Bath* (2nd ed., 1765; facsimile ed., Bath, 1969), p.238.
3   Bodleian Library, Oxford, MS. Top. Wilts. c.2, fol.29.

10   So much for John Wood the *avant garde* Arcadian garden designer. But the surprise helped to set Wood in a provincial Wiltshire context of 1734 when, for a man of his age, born in 1704, gardens would have been edging quite cautiously from the formal layouts of the 17th century towards a slightly more relaxed and eventually Arcadian solution under the directions of Charles Bridgeman and William Kent.

Bridgeman is not only a rather mysterious figure in garden history, though a highly influential one, but one with strong Wiltshire connections which I have been tracing across the county.[4] Someone with a distinguished surname but no known parents or baptismal record can often be the illegitimate but acknowledged child of a noble family. Not only do the Bridgemans cluster thickly around Bowood House for four generations, from around 1660 to 1745, when the last of them, the profligate third Sir Orlando, committed suicide in the Thames and the present Petty-Fitzmaurices took over, but the park of Whetham House, which borders Bowood Park to west, may well have been redesigned by Charles Bridgeman.[5]

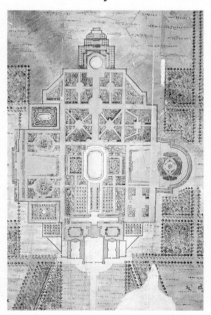

There is a 1728 map of the layout at Whetham in the Bowood muniments with Bridgeman's design signature of the stepped-back, rectangular clearings in a woodland. Similar, tentatively informal woodland glades were laid out by him at Amesbury Abbey in the same county, at Lodge Park, Sherborne in Gloucestershire and Eastbury in Dorset [fig. 3]. They are typical of that nervously geometrical response to natural features that are found in cusp gardens between the two styles.[6] These angular design features worked well with Sir John Vanbrugh's

Fig. 3

4   See Peter Willis, *Charles Bridgeman and the English Landscape Garden* (2nd ed., Newcastle-upon-Tyne, 2002).

5   See Mowl, *Wiltshire*, Chapter 5.

6   For Bridgeman's plan of Amesbury see Mowl, *Wiltshire*, colour plate 7; for his plan of Lodge Park see Timothy Mowl, *Historic Gardens of Gloucestershire* (Stroud, 2002), fig. 30; the plan of Eastbury is in the Bodleian Library, Oxford: MS. Gough Drawings, a.3 fol.10 (detail).

gloriously heavy hand in garden buildings, as at Stowe in Buckinghamshire, where Bridgeman's bold zig-zags between garden temples and rectangular canals and octagonal lakes[7] only needed the softening hand of William Kent a few years later in the 1730s to transform them into picturesque Arcadias [fig. 4].[8]

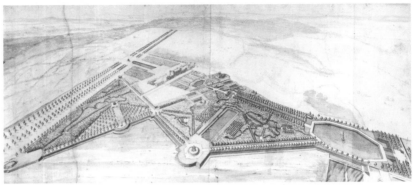

Fig. 4

Bridgeman's garden styling is unmistakable. He designed like a man who was sensitive to topography, wanted to respond to it, but was determined not to be fussy in his approach. He used complementary geometrical shapes – exedras, diamonds, circles, straight avenues, round, rectangular and octagonal waters – but above all he loved tiered amphitheatres for their Roman reference, and slammed them

down, even where they had no natural reference: in a marshy field at Standlynch (now Trafalgar House), near Salisbury, Wiltshire again, and by the lake at Claremont in Surrey, where it sticks out like a prehistoric earthwork [fig. 5].[9] It is as if he

Fig. 5

was an architect *manqué*, determined to make a park look like a building; and John Wood the Elder was, if one reads his astonishing concealed biography, *An Essay Towards a Description of Bath*, a topographer *manqué*, who was happiest when his town planning accorded with the lie of the land: hence we have his Bath, a garden city after the Bridgeman manner.

7   Bridgeman's c.1720 plan of Stowe is in the Bodleian Library, Oxford: MS. Gough Drawings, a4 f.46.
8   For Vanbrugh, Bridgeman and Stowe see Timothy Mowl, *Gentlemen & Players: Gardeners of the English Landscape* (Stroud, 2000), Chapter 6; for Vanbrugh see Christopher Ridgway & Robert Williams, *Sir John Vanbrugh and Landscape Architecture in Baroque England 1690-1730* (Stroud, 2000).
9   For Bridgeman's plan of Standlynch see Mowl, *Wiltshire*, fig. 31; for contemporary paintings of Claremont see *John Harris, The Artist and the Country House*, 1979, figs. 192a-e, and Roy Strong, *The Artist & the Garden*, 2000, fig. 293.

12

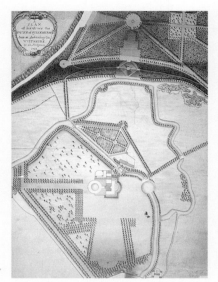

Fig. 6—

Amesbury Abbey had, and to some extent still retains, a marvellously Bath-like Bridgeman layout [fig. 6]. As well as a big stepped exedra cut into the groves on the level reaches of the park, four smaller exedra of trees. Two responding to bends in the river, one to a bend in the park wall and one bastioned out from a kite-shaped walled kitchen garden by the Avon. Cut into the 100ft bank above the river there is a great exedral-shaped crescent with a diamond of paths slashed into it and a Grotto cave at the Diamond's centre. Above this strange feature another crescent of a drive runs along the hill-top, while a stepped-back rectangle cuts into the woods and meets there one of several geometries – circles, squares and bastions – cut out of the trees, all linked by straight avenues. It is like a re-run of Wood's Bath, but with trees not houses. A walk through these avenues and tree plantations has echoes of the way Brock Street works with the great surprise geometries at either end: the amphitheatrical King's Circus with absolutely no exterior reference, and the sublime Royal Crescent with its arms entirely open to the valley views, its shape coolly picking up what the elder Wood would have called 'a dent' in the hillside.[10]

Charles Bridgeman loved crescents. It was as if he could not see a promising steep bank without wanting to carve one out of it. The park at Standlynch runs for half a mile along and above the Wiltshire South Avon, and at one point where the river bends sharply away and widens out Bridgeman, working in 1733 to provide a suitable setting for the London merchant, Sir Peter Vanderput's new house, excavated a 75ft wide crescent out of a 50ft cliff. It was probably intended to function, along with the widening of the river,

10 Wood, *Essay*, p.4.

as an echo; even now, grown over with big trees, it seems to have acoustic properties. Otherwise it was dug out at considerable expense with no other aim than to make an harmonious impact upon nature and to give visitors something to look down on from the viewing mound raised above it from all that excavated earth. In 1733 his amphitheatre down by the river would have been visible.

Nikolaus Pevsner is very perceptive about this 'surprise' quality in semi-formal planning. He takes Walter Ison quite severely to task for suggesting that Bath lacks 'a completely homogeneous development'. The Woods, Pevsner observes, 'knew exactly what they were doing'; what Ison describes as 'the sense of anti-climax' in some Bath architecture is instead 'a calculated means of achieving variety and surprise'.[11] This is all true, but then Pevsner, on the very edge of a shrewd observation, misses the chronological connection and the point he should be making. He is absolutely correct when he writes that 'the aesthetics of planning in C18 England apply to the gardens and the park rather than the city'; but then he lists all the wrong influences: Pope, Shenstone, of all people, a sinuous park wanderer who avoided straight lines and geometry, Whately, Gilpin, Uvedale Price and Richard Payne Knight, all right off the mark.[12] But then Pevsner disapproved of the aristocracy and formal garden hangovers, so Bridgeman would not have been in his sights. Wood's Bath is great planning, but surprise grandeurs were not the influences that Pevsner was looking for; he inclined to the picturesque and the informal.

Reading the lovingly observed detail of Wood's topographical survey of Bath's surroundings it is obvious that, like Bridgeman, he looked for basic, hard shapes, the essence of an area not the details: Walcot 'being the Shape of the Letter Y inverted'; Charlcomb 'the two shorter Sides of a plain Triangle'; 'two Villages…answer the Angles of an Equilateral Triangle'; South Stoke 'lying in a Square Form'; Corston 'in the shape of the Letter T'; Solford (Saltford) 'forms one compleat Line opening at the Bottom like the Fork of the Letter Y' and Woolley 'a Figure like the Letter T'.[13]

Prior Park, the vast showpiece of Wood's own designing, ought, as a neo-Palladian house, poised on a 'dent' of steep hillside,

11 Nikolaus Pevsner, *The Buildings of England: North Somerset and Bristol,* London 1958, p.94-5.
12 Ibid., p.95.
13 Wood, *Essay,* pp.90-6.

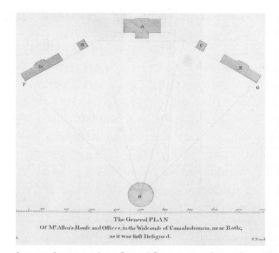

The General PLAN
Of Mr Allen's House and Offices, in the Widcomb of Camalodunum, near Bath;
as it was first Designed.

Fig. 7

to have been centred between the usual Palladian quadrant arms, their curves responding to the easy flow of the topography. But instead Wood applied a quite harsh Bridgemanesque geometry to the site, illustrating his vision with a 'Plan of this Seat as it was first intended', lettered to make his intentions quite clear [fig. 7]. By this plan 'the Extent of the Seat from F to G was proposed to answer that of three Sides of a Duodecagon, inscribed within a Circle of a Quarter of a Mile Diameter'.[14] Finally, so that there should be no mistake about that mystic circle, he persuaded his patron, Ralph Allen, to create 'H', an exact circular pool of water, carved and dammed up out of the hillside at considerable expense and entirely contrary to the lie of the land.[15] But it marked where a great compass point would have had to be inserted to describe that 'Circle of a Quarter of a Mile Diameter'. His scheme was not primarily Roman or Palladian, but a geometric figure first and foremost. And so his landscape perceptions continue throughout the book, not in colours, church towers or trees, but Vs, Ts, squares, circles and crosses.

What would, if Ralph Allen had not frustrated him, have been his boldest transposition of a Bridgeman garden feature to town planning was his scheme for the 'Haven of Bath'.[16] Bridgeman had, by the early 1720s, laid out a grand octagonal basin in the park at Stowe as the climax to the main avenue cutting down south from the house. Wood proposed an even larger octagonal basin in the one area [fig. 8], The Ham, level enough to take such a feature. Recorded only in the rare and separately published 'Part the Third' of the first edition of his *Description of Bath* (undated, but probably of the early

14 Ibid., p.96.
15 For Anthony Walker's 1752 engraving which shows the bones of Wood's landscape design at Prior Park see Timothy Mowl & Brian Earnshaw, *John Wood: Architect of Obsession* (Bath, 1988), p.102; see also Gillian Clarke, *Prior Park: A Compleat Landscape* (Bath, 1987).
16 Wood, *Essay*, p.4.

1740s), it would have been an imperial *capriccio* rather than a Royal Forum, and an architectural prodigy to rival the King's Circus and the Royal Crescent.[17] An enormous rectangle, 1,040ft long by 624ft broad of 'Porticos' was to be bisected exactly by the straight and canalized Avon, with no thought for the river's natural curves. To centre this space the river was to be disciplined out into 'an Octangular Bason of Water': the 'Haven' and new hub of the city.[18] On each side of the river were to be piazzas 'for People to celebrate their Feasts and Festivals, and carry on their Commerce'.[19] So it would have been lined with quays for market boats and pleasure craft. Above the 'Porticos' were to be 'Terrases of fifty feet broad, before four lines of Building, intended to be erected in a Rich and Elegant Manner'.[20]

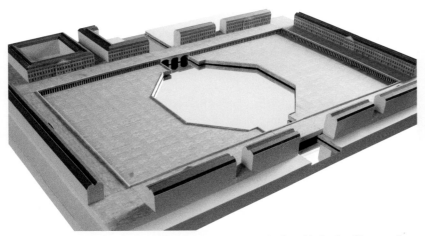

Fig. 8

Two bridges would have been needed to link the 'lines of Building'; the Avon itself, tamed into a garden feature, would have dominated the Forum. From a note written on 27 April 1734 to William Brydges it appears that Wood was even hoping to entice royalty to take a second seat in Bath with such an imperial project. 'There is talk (with very good foundation)', he wrote, 'that the King will have a House built here'.[21] Yet for all this proposed geometric grandeur Wood still saw his city in garden terms, but Bridgemanesque garden terms: 'A Region that sets Paradise itself before one's Eyes…the

17 Later, in 1740, Wood produced a modified version of this scheme, confining it to the north bank of the Avon; see Mowl & Earnshaw, *John Wood*, p.138 (Nottingham University Library, Manvers MS. 4184).
18 Wood, *Essay, Part the Third*, p.87.
19 Ibid.
20 Ibid.
21 Manuscript letter in Bath Reference Library.

16 very *Elysium Fields* of the Antients'.[22] Viewed from 'the Summit of Beeching Cliff' it would, he claimed, 'appear much the same that *Virgil* declares *Carthage* to have appeared to *Aeneas*'.[23] Carthage, however, had no 'Octangular Bason'; Wood had caught that feature from Bridgeman's Stowe.

To understand Wood's town planning he has to be seen as a 17th century man prone to grandiose formalities who lived on into the 18th century with its growing appreciation of natural beauties. Bridgeman's parallel design career helped him to span the two moods. That never-achieved Royal Forum with the Avon at its centre would have been of the earlier century: a place, he claimed, 'where Kings were wont to Convene the People and I will endeavour to give it an Air of Magnificence, equal to any Thing of its Kind'.[24] But in his 18th century sensibility Wood revelled in the natural beauty of his Avon valley:

> The Elevation of these Hills is such, that their Summits command a Country so exceeding beautiful, and of such vast Extent, that the Eye that views it, and the Mind that considers it with Attention, can never be enough satisfied.[25]

His vast Royal Forum around an 'Octangular Bason' was never realised, but the fragment of it that was built, featuring the Grand Parade on the south side of the Parade Gardens, was to be 'the principal Place of publick Resort in the City', not for its market or theatre, but because its houses would 'reflect a Beauty to each other', not of masonry, but of the view of Solsbury Hill, geometrically appreciated again which 'though Triangular at Top, appears like the Frustrum of a Conical Mountain'.[26] A frustrum was a technical surveyor's term for a horizontally truncated pyramid or cone. Wood was much more adept as a surveyor than as a joiner, the profession to which he is usually linked. In the early 18th century joiners would supervise the practicalities of house building, but when Wood supervised the building of houses for the Duke of Chandos at St John's Hospital there was chaos and recrimination.[27] When he, with his surveyor's eye, planned out that taxing hillside north of the city, he was the master of superb surprises. Meanwhile teams of artisans supervised the actual house building.

22 Wood, *Essay,* p.440.
23 Ibid., p.441.
24 Wood, *Essay, Part the Second,* p.17.
25 Wood, *Essay,* p.54.
26 Ibid., p.351.
27 See Mowl & Earnshaw, *John Wood,* Chaper 2.

What was so innovatory and great – the word has to be used as John Wood is the unacknowledged greatest English architect of the first half of the century, an epic poet in Bath stonework – was the way in which he soared above his London training almost as soon as he had left the capital in 1725. London, like all the rest of Western Europe, limited town planning to conventional squares. Louis XIV's circular Place des Victoires in Paris is a mere open *rond-point,* a meeting of ways, not a demanding and glorious confinement like the amphitheatric King's Circus. When he returned to Bath, falling like a creative thunderbolt on that self-satisfied city of peasant Baroque, Wood thought in amphitheatres. There were to be a Forum, a Circus and a Gymnasium, but his very first scheme, exhibited in April 1730 at a breakfast and ball at Dame Lindsey's Assembly House, was 'a grand *Circus*': an amphitheatre with three roads branching out from it, a trinitarian symbol planned almost exactly like the ultimate King's Circus, which would not be begun until February 1754, the year of his death.[28] He proposed it for the orchard to the south-east of the Abbey and, reached directly by a bridge over the Avon, it could have been impact-making.

Sensing opposition he began to plan Queen Square in the same year, taking the first leases on 17 June 1730. But that was only after a major design *volte-face.* He had been intending, not a revived city of Bladud and the Celtic Druids, pre-Roman, patriotic and mythical, but a reconstruction of 'the Street called the *Principia*', a 100ft wide way based upon that of a supposed, but in fact imaginary, Roman legionary camp, with Wood Street at the head of a T and Barton Street its 50ft wide downward stroke.[29] Earl Tylney, Colen Campbell's patron and the builder of that distinctly commonplace Campbell design for Wanstead House, Essex, had backed the scheme and bought the central house in the group of three proudly featured in the *Essay* opposite page 344. But speculators moved in, land prices soared and Wood had to abandon his frankly inappropriate legionary camp.

So what were the forces behind Wood's town planning, over and above his surveyor's eye for topographical shapes? His few years working for Robert Benson, Lord Bingley at Bramham Park in

---

28 Wood, *Essay*, p.245; for a drawing of the scheme see Mowl & Earnshaw, *John Wood*, p.70. The geometric difference between this scheme and the final King's Circus is that the entry points for the three roads are set at the points of an isosceles triangle, whereas those at the King's Circus from an equilateral triangle. For Wood's Christian beliefs, strongly slanted towards Freemasonry, see his *The Origin of Building, or the Plagiarism of the Heathens Detected,* 1741.

29 Ibid., p.168. For the influence of this legionary camp on Wood's town planning see William Bertram, *The Origins and Building of Queen Square, Bath,* Architectural Association thesis, 1963.

18

Yorkshire had resulted in a detailed estate plan, published in 1731, but drawn in 1726-7.[30] Bingley's park planning had been conventional and uninspired, though his park buildings, like his house, are excellent. Straight avenues criss-cross straight avenues, with three *rond-points* to break the tedium, so the layout is unlikely to have influenced the young surveyor. Wood's first planning drive was predictably Roman in a period when kings and lords almost invariably had themselves sculpted as togaed Roman senators and thought Augustan. Both the Circus for the Abbey Orchard and the Wood Street *Principia* were Roman in inspiration. Underlying the King's Circus, however, was the Freemasonic symbolism of the Trinity. It was a theme that Wood was going to cling to right up to his deathbed.

If we look for other influences upon Wood's planning in his last years and his son's faithful continuance in those plans, Bridgeman still offered more to Wood as he balanced the Roman and the Freemasonic and as his antiquarian obsessions deepened over Druid prehistory.[31] Wood's inspired scheme for a new Royal Forum on The Ham between the Grand Parade and the Avon came to nothing, but its extraordinary octagonal port on the river owed more than a hint to Bridgeman's great octagonal lake at the end of the main vista at Stowe in Buckinghamshire. Bridgeman was still hankering after 17th century formal gestures rather than any relaxed and curvaceous garden scheme. Finally there were the works at The Moot, Downton in Wiltshire [fig. 9], with its atmospheric park, wrapped about a massive Norman castle motte of King Stephen's reign. The layout has never been firmly attributed to Bridgeman,

but it is barely two miles from his amphitheatre and crescent at Trafalgar House and it boasts a perfect amphitheatre of its own, carved out with terraced steps from the old castle mound and perfectly fronting a trilobal lake. The date offered for it, 1733, would have made it an encouraging influence on Wood.[32]

Fig. 9

30 The Bramham plan is illustrated in Mowl & Earnshaw, *John Wood*, p.19.
31 This was basically an offshoot of his Freemasonry, Prince Bladud having taken over the role of Pythagoras, whom Masons believed had taken up the design of one of the three sacred temples of the Jews which had succeeded each other in Jerusalem over a roughly 900 year period.
32 1733 is the probable date of Bridgeman's new designs for Standlynch.

So Wood still held on to the memory of his old lost Circus on the Abbey Orchard, kept its trinity of three roads, but enlarged its diameter by 58ft to give it exactly the dimensions of the larger stone circle at Stanton Drew. This he had measured, and believed to have been the site of a college of the ancient Druids. In further homage to his entirely fanciful pre-Roman, Celtic metropolis of Bath he crowned the King's Circus with the acorns of the Druids – the 'oak men' – instead of the usual classical finials of urns or pineapples. There, in one strange circle we have Wood's obsessions: Roman in its three classical orders, Druid in its dimensions and in many of the symbols carved over its Doric frieze, Christian and Freemasonic in its trinitarian symbolism and in its supposed reference to Zerubbabel's Second, and just possibly circular, Temple at Jerusalem. But essentially the King's Circus is one of Bridgeman's amphitheatres providing a classical surprise at the end of Gay, Brock and Bennett Streets, with avenues, not of trees, but of houses.

As for the Royal Crescent at the far end of Brock Street, John Wood the Younger's wise tribute to his father's vision, that was a tribute in itself, a tribute to the valley vistas that Wood the Elder loved so well. It faced outwards, planned so that there should never be any interruption, to enjoy 'those Hills that surround the hot Springs', where Nature seems to have had a Spiral Motion, so as to form a Kind of Volute'.[33] And if even the Woods could hardly rise to a spiral street plan, then there was still, in the centre of the view, 'looking like a vast Heap of Earth whose Northern Side had been undermined so as to slip down, and leave a stupendous Cliff above in the Shape of a large Cressant', the Beechen Cliff, a natural crescent to inspire, in true Bridgemanesque spirit, an artificial one.[34]

33 Wood, *Essay*, p.55.
34 Ibid., p.52.

20

A benevolent friendship, John Wood and Ralph Allen: Bath as a capitalist city
Cathryn Spence

Fig. 10

Fig. 11

The accepted image of John Wood [fig. 10] is as the cantankerous, but driven architect. Ralph Allen [fig. 11], on the other hand, is seen as the generous humanitarian, immortalised as Squire Allworthy in Henry Fielding's *Tom Jones* (oddly accepted as a positive personification). Both men were entrepreneurs, prosperous businessmen whose shared vision and mutual furtherance ensured their individual success and the birth of a fashionable city. Their's was an extraordinary partnership of fateful synchronicity. Through their respective interests, Wood and Allen capitalised on the ownership of stone production, the means and control of its distribution, and the provision of a market. Only the combination of both men, in Bath at the same time, could have resulted in this celebrated city of architecture in stone.

In the same year that Ralph Allen (1693-1764) was made an Honorary Freeman of the City and elected a Councilman, Wood sent him his plan for Bath. That was in 1725, but although involved in a number of ventures in Bath, Wood did not take lodgings in the city until 1727. Why did he wait two years to return? To work in Bath, Wood also needed to be a Freeman. The Corporation upheld a law that prevented outsiders from carrying on trade in the city and taking income away from the Freemen of Bath. In 1725 the Council pointed out that no one could gain their liberty to ply their trade unless they were apprenticed to a Freeman for seven years, were of noble birth or able to pay a substantial fee. How did Wood overcome this? He was not of noble birth, nor was he in a position to pay a fee. We know he was working in London as a 'joyner' by the time he was 17, so he had not stayed in Bath long enough to have completed a seven-year apprenticeship before the decreed age of 21.[1] Even if Wood had served his apprenticeship, in his own words, 'the freedom thus obtained is to be lost by any person who shall depart and live out of the City by the space of a twelve month and a day'.[2]

It became Allen's practice to pay for his masons to have the right to work in other cities. In 1730 he paid £210 for seven of his men to get 'leave of the City [of London]...to come and Work within their Libertys' on the St Bartholomew's Hospital contract.[3] He also arranged for his tied masons to be given liberty to work on the

---

1 He is referred to as 'John Wood of the parish of St Anne Westminster in the county of Middlesex Joyner' in the Harley Estate Records. British Museum, Add. MS. 18241, f.36. Timothy Mowl & Brian Earnshaw, *John Wood: Architect of Obsession*, (Bath, 1988), p.13.
2 John Wood, *An Essay Towards a Description of Bath*, 1765 ed., (Kingsmead Reprints, 1969), p.406.
3 John Wood, *A Description of the Exchange of Bristol* (Bath, 1745), p.18.

Bristol Exchange, despite the complaints of the Freemen of Bristol. As the building was financed by the Chamber, the Freemen argued that they should have been the ones to build it and not Allen's masons from Bath. Wood levied any shortcomings firmly at the feet of 'the common Freemen of the City [who] claiming a right of trampling upon the Work...will sufficiently answer for any faults that may appear in the performance of the ornamental part of the building.'[4] It is highly probable, therefore, that trusting Wood's competence, Allen arranged for his freedom so he could return and work in Bath. Wood knew Allen through the work he had undertaken from 1723 in London on the Cavendish Estate. Allen owned a townhouse there and it is likely that Wood worked on it. Undoubtedly, Wood knew of Allen's success with the cross-and-bye postal operation and his subsequent authority within Bath Corporation. In early 1727 Allen engaged Wood to design the additions to his house in Lilliput Alley, Bath. In the same year, the influential James Brydges, 1st Duke of Chandos, may also have been instrumental in arranging Wood's freedom, as he engaged him to work on the re-development of St John's Hospital, Bath. The emergence of Wood's new, self-termed title of Surveyor, was probably devised by one or all of these men and quite possibly made his working-liberty easier to attain. Until the second half of the 18th century the terms of surveyor and architect were interchangeable, but as a profession it did not comply fully with an apprenticeship scheme.

Soon after Wood and Allen's initial correspondence in 1725 and the possible onset of their business relations, Wood was able to pay a substantial amount of money towards the cost of common sewers on the property at No. 1 Oxford Street, London. He had been quite seriously in arrears on the ground rent for about four years.[5] Suddenly he is not only able to invest £14 in the sewers, but he is also given as the original leaseholder for not merely No. 1, but numbers 2, 3 and 4 Oxford Street as well.[6] Robert Benson, 1st Lord Bingley, had employed him, in some capacity, in 1724 and 1725 and perhaps payment came through sporadically.[7] Nevertheless, the settling of his debts allowed Wood to move on to designing his major projects for Bath.

4   Ibid.
5   Harley Estate Records. British Museum, Add. MS. 18241; Mowl & Earnshaw, *John Wood*, p.14.
6   Add. MS. 18243. Ibid.
7   Hoare's Bank, Account Books G and H. Ibid.

Bath's success as a resort in the 18th century is due to the capitalist investment in its amenities and its accessibility. Through his relationship with Allen, Wood was involved in the production of both. His plan for Bath included a scheme for improving the River Avon as 'a necessary prelude to the architectural developments' he visualised.[8] In May 1724, John Hobbs, a Bristol deal merchant, set up a stock company to improve the River Avon and to encourage more economic trade. Allen was one of the three treasurers involved. Work to deepen and widen the River Avon between Bath and Bristol began in 1725 and Allen ensured he had control of the project. He was one of the 32 shareholders, but so was his brother-in-law, Anthony Rodney Buckeridge of Ware, Hertfordshire and no less than six other family members. Through his involvement with Allen the young Wood, who had no capital at this time, was offered the contract for a 600-yard stretch at Twerton. It was during this contract, signed on 10 March 1727, that Wood claimed he introduced the spade to Bath:

> *For the better execution of the work I forthwith procured labourers, that had been employed on the Chelsea water-Works, and sent them down to Bath to dig the canal I had undertaken; 'till which time the real use of the spade was unknown in, or about the City, and the removal of earth was then reduced to a third part of what it formerly cost.* [9]

It seems that Wood's inability to charm officials was apparent even with this early engagement. Difficulties between him and Edward Marchant, the main contractor, saw Wood's contract terminated in July 1727. Being paid just over £55 for the work, this could hardly have been a profitable venture for Wood. The first barge travelled from Bristol to Bath only five months later in December 1727. However in that year Wood was already busily employed. He was working on the St John's Hospital scheme for Chandos (afflicted with its own well-documented problems),[10] at Tyberton Church in Herefordshire and on Allen's townhouse in Bath.[11]

Not an enthusiastic participant or spectator of sport, Wood was thrilled when Allen acquired a new house near the Abbey in Lilliput Alley as the land for the garden was taken from the town's bowling green and so put an end to 'Smock Racing and Pig Racing, playing at Foot-Ball and running with the Feet in Bags'.[12] Wood's

8 Wood, *Essay*, p.232.

9 Ibid., p.241.

10 James Brydges, First Duke of Chandos. Letterbooks, Huntingdon Library, California. This collection contains 108 letters to Wood, copied for the Duke's reference by his secretary. Very few of Wood's replies survive. The problems with this project are detailed in Mowl & Earnshaw, *John Wood*, Chapter 2.

11 See page 103 and catalogue entry 17 and 19.

12 Wood, *Essay*, p.244.

24

design for the addition to the north front of this house was carried out whilst he was in London, during the spring of 1727 [Cat. No. 17]. He added a storey and a Palladian façade with blind balustrades, carved festoons, an ornamental pediment and four giant Corinthian columns. Wood wrote that 'it consists of a Basement Story sustaining a double Story under the Crowning; and this is surmounted by an Attick, which created a sixth Rate House, and a Sample for the greatest Magnificence that was ever proposed by me for our City Houses.' [13] However, Allen engaged another builder to actually undertake the construction. Perhaps, whilst Allen appreciated the genius of Wood and was bound to him in business, he was not about to risk his own home to his infamous impracticality.

Still, Wood was a good publicist, for himself, for Allen and for Bath, which in turn was self-gratifying. In 1736 James Leake, the Bath bookseller, printed a map of Bath, 'Copied from the Original Survey of Mr John Wood of Bath, Architect' [fig. 21, p.36]. It included an invitation from Wood to come and enjoy what Bath had to offer. This comprised of what he described as a good municipal government, the bronze head of Apollo (actually Minerva),[14] the Assembly Rooms, the obelisk in Orange Grove and Allen's crane, which Wood advised was a 'A Masterpiece of Mechanism'. A further enticement was the chance to buy stone direct from Allen and, therefore, at a quarter of the price. It continued:

> For the Convenience of Builders, Mr Wood intends, very soon, to set up a Deal Yard...in which Persons may be supply'd with the best of Norway goods...and for their Encouragement, shall be directed in the Use & Choice of their Materials, from whence great Advantages will arise (at least ten pounds in every hundred) to the Buyer.[15]

Wood was extraordinary in his ability to marry the often opposing characteristics of commercial awareness and obsessive creativity.

Until 1736, when the dividends from the development of Queen Square started to accumulate, John Wood had to borrow money to fund his other developments. After the death of his brother-in-law in 1734, Allen encouraged his widowed sister-in-law, Ann Buckeridge, to invest her inheritance in Wood. In 1735 it was agreed that for the sum of £1,500 Wood would give Ann a mortgage

13 Ibid., p.245.

14 The head of Minerva was uncovered in July 1727 when workmen were digging a new sewer at High Street. Wood refers to the sculpture as being 'that of a beardless young man with long curled hair; and so the Grecian sculptures always represented Apollo'. Ibid., p.159.

15 James Leake, Bath, 1736.

at 5% on some ground-rent property in Bath. By 1744 Ann Buckeridge's loan to Wood had grown to a mighty £2,600. This investment coincides with what has been described as Wood's most pivotal years. He had started Prior Park, was raising subscriptions for St Mary's Chapel in Queen Square[16] and had embarked on the restoration of Llandaff Cathedral.[17] This essential financial aid, arranged by Allen, propelled Wood in to a different league of speculative development and its subsequent rewards.

The strongest bond between Wood and Allen came through their mutual love of Bath stone and equally their mistrust of the jobbing mason. In 1726, the year after he received Wood's plan for the city, Allen started to buy up the quarries on Combe Down from Mary Wiltshire, Milo Smith and Thomas Greenway. As a result of buying the quarry from Greenway, Allen inherited Richard Jones who was to become his Clerk of Works. It was Combe Down stone that Wood used in the majority of his projects. The rescued balustrade from Queen Square and the two acorns from the Circus in the collection at the Building of Bath Museum confirm this.[18] As demand increased Allen later bought and operated quarries at Odd Down and Bathampton.

Wood obviously promoted Bath stone as his material of choice when tendering for business. In 1730 Allen won the contract to provide stone for St Bartholomew's Hospital in central London [fig. 12]. The hospital Governors included two important colleagues of Wood's: the Duke of Chandos and Robert Gay.[19] It is also telling

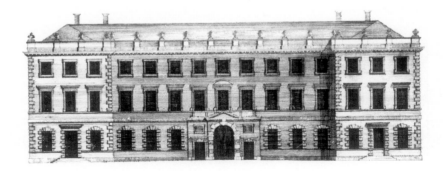

Fig. 12
Initial design for the elevation of the North Wing of St Bartholomew's Hospital, James Gibbs, 1728

16 See catalogue entry 23.
17 See catalogue, p.68.
18 See catalogue entries 20 and 44.
19 The St Bartholomew project was troubled and Allen was often forced to make concessions to the Governors on cost. He made a number of reductions and donations and estimated that his input came to over £2,000. His original quote was only £1,700.

26

that Allen won the contract to supply the stone for the Exchange at Bristol once Wood was engaged as the architect. Allen was paid over £1,327 for the stone he supplied for this project. Wood was so dedicated to the use of natural stone that he turned down a lucrative contract. In 1737, when asked to design a Seal factory in Widcombe for John Wicksted, Wood deplored of the engineer's plan to erect the building using common stone, plastering its surface, and painting it to look like brickwork.[20] 'Such an instance of whim and caprice' exclaimed Wood, 'that when I got the draughts I had made into my possession, I never parted with them again'.[21]

When he took over the freestone quarries Allen's plan was to reduce the price of the material and, therefore, to encourage consumption. He achieved this in a number of ways. Chiefly, in 1731, he introduced the renowned stone-carriages and tramway which transported the stone from the quarries, 500ft above the River Avon, down Ralph Allen's Drive, to Dolemead wharf below [fig. 13].[22]

This cut the cost of a ton of stone by a quarter. According to Jones, Allen's investment in the tramway, carriages and the crane that lifted the stone onto the barges was £10,000. Jones' manuscript autobiography states that 1,800 tonnes of Bath freestone left the wharf annually.[23] Allen's investment saved the production £4,500

Fig. 13   Detail from *A South East Prospect of Bath*, Samuel and Nathanial Buck, 1734

a year and so it had almost paid for itself within two. It was such a success that Bath stone's old rival Portland stone had to reduce its cost by a third so that it could continue to compete.

Both Allen and Wood did not like the separation of the free and rough masons. According to Wood, neither band respected the other's trade and, as a consequence, neither treated the stone blocks well, with the result that they were often put together with snags and untidy joints and mouldings. Allen's later insistence on sending his own masons, such as Thomas Omer and William Biggs, to

---

20 Wood's design relates to Moses' Tabernacle.
21 Wood, *Essay*, p.423.
22 Allen had got the idea for the tramway from the Northumberland coal mines.
23 'The Life of Richard Jones who for many years was in the Service of the Late Ralph Allen of Prior Park', Bath Central Library. 926 B. MSS, B920Jon.

important assignments in London and Bristol, illustrated his need for quality control. The free masons, however, initiated a far worse crime. Wood writes that when opportunity allowed they blended 'the good and bad stone together', thereby 'disgracing a material which, in truth, is fit for the walls of a palace for the greatest Prince in Europe'.[24]

Not long after he acquired the quarries, Wood tells us that Allen turned his attention to 'the domestic Masons Trade of Bath, and proposed to lower the rates for all manner of Workmanship… but by finding them constant Employ, and Paying them their Wages regularly every Week', he sought a more viable operation.[25] Under his ownership the established independent masons either had to adopt his new regime or they find themselves without work. The subsequent shortfall in skilled labour was solved by Wood. With the promise of guaranteed work Wood invited his old colleagues down from Yorkshire. As a consequence Wood earned himself instant loyalty from the workforce, whilst Allen was put in the powerful position of not having to be at the mercy of the old style masons. The continuing commercial prosperity of this partnership hinged on the tense awareness that for either man to break this equilibrium would undoubtedly be economically ruinous for both of them.

Allen also reduced expenditure 'by a Saving to the Workmen of all the Time they lost in going between their Habitations in and about the City, and the Quarries in the external Brow of Camalodunum.'[26] He did this by settling at least some of his labour force into tied cottages which Wood designed for him in 'two small Towns to receive the two Sets of People thus to be employed.'[27] These two rows of houses could not possibly have housed the entire workforce, so some qualification must have recommended some over others.

The accommodation that Allen offered his artisans was modern, of good standard and distinguished design. The two 'towns' survive today and are interesting for both their architectural and social concerns. They are possibly the oldest surviving examples of industrial housing. Nonetheless, free enterprise depends on control. This was not a philanthropic gesture. 'This was the very purest kind

---

24 Wood, *Essay*, p.425.
25 Ibid.
26 Ibid.
27 Ibid.

28

of capitalism. Wood needed cheap, well-cut stone. Allen wanted an expanding local market for his goods. Only the masons stood in the way.'[28]

The 'towns' are made up of Wood's stalwart: the terrace. They consist of ten and eleven houses and are about two miles apart. One set is at the foot of Prior Park Road, near the River Avon [fig. 14] and the other on the top of Combe Down. They were obviously considered together as they are thematically related. The top houses were designed for the quarrymen, who were 'concerned in digging, raising, and transporting the unwrought stone down to a common yard by the water side'.[29] The men could gain access to the mine at the rear of these cottages from Davidge's Bottom. They are double fronted and two-storied with the central Dial House [fig. 15] having a triangular pediment with a ball and sundial above the porch. This was originally the foreman's house and it contained a small chapel or prayer room. It was in this house that Allen's Clerk of Works, Richard Jones, the fourth figure in *The Four Bath Worthies* painting [Cat. No. 16], lived. He earned £45 a year and reputedly constructed the two 'towns' from Wood's designs.

In 1780, Edmund Rack, then secretary of the Bath and West Society, wrote that, 'the entire village of Combe Down consists of 11

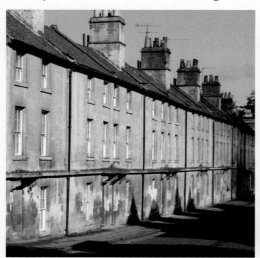

Fig. 14

Fig. 15

28 Mowl & Earnshaw, *John Wood*, p.43.
29 Wood, *Essay*, p.425.

houses built by Ralph Allen in 1729 for his quarrymen' [fig. 16]. Jones
confirms this when he wrote that there were no houses on the bare
expanse of the hill-top and it was very exposed to the elements.
Earl de Montalt, who married one of Allen's nieces, renovated and
enlarged these top cottages and the terrace was subsequently
renamed De Montalt Place. The terrace is still noteworthy due to its
elegance and unity.

Fig. 16
Combe Down, Bath. Thomas
Robins, c.1757-9

    The masons who worked the stone were to have proper
sheds in a yard in the area known as the Dolemeads, as well as
houses nearby at Withy Bed. These lower houses, now known as
Ralph Allen's Row, were positioned near the yard at Widcombe
Wharf. They were also built by Jones, but erected later in 1736. There
are distinctive end units, with the eight middle houses linked by
shared porches and a pilaster strip [fig. 17].

Fig. 17

The principles that
governed Wood's design of these
two 'towns' were the same as
for his larger, more grandiose
projects. Just as in his design for
the North front of Queen Square,
there is a unified harmony
created by his use of a 'palace'
façade with architectural devices
serving to emphasise the central
house or 'grand' entrance. In *The
Origin of Building* Wood explains
that the Israelites built cottages
around Moses' Tabernacle and

30

Solomon's Temple, and to Wood, even these small structures could achieve the distinction of beauty through the application of the orders. 'Will not such an edifice, as small as it is, be beautiful?'[30] The Combe Down terrace houses have their own front gardens, whilst both 'towns' have distinct and separate entrance doors. According to Wood a small stone house on the side of Bowden Hill in Wiltshire [fig. 18], not far from the London Road, was the source for the roofs for these cottages as well as for the roofs for the lodge cottages at

the gates of Allen's carriage road. The roofs were originally laid with slabs of stone. Wood would have known this type of traditional roof covering from his days working at St John's Hospital. It was also his intention to have the roof at

Fig. 18

the Bristol Exchange in stone, rather than the Cornish slate that was eventually used.

The cottages tied a section of the masons to Allen, his quarry and his conditions. In return they had accommodation, steady work and a regular, although lower, wage. The cost of Bath stone was driven down by a further 10% and piecework became less common. The obvious advantage to Wood was the regular production and increased quantity of stone, which in turn meant his material of choice was cheaper.

Allen's competitor, Milo Smith, strove hard to stay in business, but eventually his quarries were bought out by Allen. The master masons also tried to undermine Allen's control by undercutting his prices. Allen's commitment went deep though. During the harsh winter of 1739-40 he created work in his quarries for hundreds of labourers to relieve the distress. This was a charitable act, but also an assurance of the status quo. Both Allen and Wood were involved in other charitable acts, such as the foundation of the General Hospital.

Humphry Thayer, a wealthy druggist and surgeon who owned land in Bath, acted as treasurer for the appeal to fund the

30 John Wood, *The Origin of Building, or the Plagiarism of the Heathens Detected*, 1741, Book I. In 1781, Wood's son echoed his father's principles when he wrote in *A Series of Plans for Cottages or Habitations of the Labourer, either in Husbandry, or the Mechanic Arts, Adapted as well to Towns as to the Country* that 'cottages should be well built, with the best materials. By building the cottages with regularity, beauty is forthcoming, but under no circumstances', urged John Wood the Younger should 'these cottages be fine'. Both father and son specified, either in writing or action, that workers cottages should be built in pairs, each with a proportionally sized garden.

proposed General Hospital. Thayer instructed Wood to not only design the hospital, but also to find a suitable location on which to site it. The significance of this project was that the Hospital was central to Wood's unrealised scheme for an Imperial Gymnasium, as projected in his *Essay*. Wood originally offered the committee, of which Allen was a member, two designs, both requiring a similar sized plot, both with a bath filled with thermal water flowing down a conduit from the Hot Bath. One version was quadrangular, the other, significantly, was circular. The trustees of the projected Bath Hospital decided to publish Wood's design in the April of 1731 in the hope of encouraging further donations to the project [fig. 19].

Fig. 19

Unfortunately the committee eventually favoured the rather uninspiring rectangular block design. Now situated on a cramped site, the original design is marred by John Palmer's 1793 additional attic storey. The commission had allowed for experimentation and the testing of architectural ideas and, if indeed Wood was a Freemason, it complied with one of the driving principles of Freemasonry: that of charitable care for the community as a whole.

By May 1742 the Hospital was complete and the regulations for admission were printed and distributed across the country.

Beneficiaries had to be recommended by their parish and be invalids or cripples who were expected to benefit from the waters. Not undermining Allen and Wood's charitable involvement, a hospital of this nature ensured that the unsightly visitor to Bath was accommodated away from the more fashionable clientele. It also allowed for more progressive policing of those crippled vagrants who unsettled society. It was important to both Allen and Wood that society wanted to come to Bath and take advantage of the amenities that it had to offer, the provision of which secured their continuing financial success.

Allen and Wood also shared personnel. Thomas Omer, who had worked for Wood and would later share his house in Queen Square, was taken on by Allen.[31] His reputation was so good that Allen's friend, Alexander Pope, 'wished to borrow him' in early 1740; but the timing was inconvenient.[32] Allen needed Omer to represent him when tendering for the contract for the Bristol Exchange and Market.[33] In June, once Allen had won the contract, he considered it convenient to send Omer to Twickenham where Pope employed him to finish his Grotto. In 1741, Pope borrowed another of Allen and Wood's men, the stonemason Thomas Biggs, who was the brother of William who had represented Allen during the building of St Bartholomew's Hospital. William Biggs assembled and arranged for the stone to be transported to London. He also worked for Wood on the Bristol Exchange in 1742-3 and subscribed to two copies of Wood's 1745 *Description of the Exchange of Bristol.* Another of Allen's tied masons to subscribe to this publication was Robert Parsons of Widcombe. He was involved with the house carving at the Exchange. Other subscribers linked to Allen were brothers Benjamin and Daniel Greenway, marble and freestone masons, who made the vases for the Bristol Exchange, and Richard Knapp, freestone mason. The list of subscribers, 300 in total, is of interest. They include Richard 'Beau' Nash, the artist William Hoare and Thomas Attwood, a plumber and glazier from Bath and another of the Avon Navigation shareholders. Allen is not listed, but it was in his nature to subscribe anonymously, as he did so for publications by both Fielding and Pope.[34] Of note is Sir James Creed of Greenwich's subscription for

---

31 Omer is often referred to as a joyner and a carpenter and he certainly worked on the altarpiece at Tyberton. However, he must also have been an experienced stonemason and quite possibly a clerk of works to have represented Allen as he did, and to have been employed by Pope.

32 *The Correspondence of Alexander Pope,* George Sherburn (ed.), 1956, IV.

33 As we have seen Wood usually helped Allen by representing him when he was pitching for a contract to supply Bath stone. However, Wood had already won the contract to design the Exchange and it would certainly have been seen as a serious conflict of interest, or even corruption, should he have represented Allen and Bath stone in this instance. This is also the time of Wood and Allen's reputed quarrel.

seven copies. His design for a pump was praised in the publication as Wood explained that he had used a similar design at Bristol and in his house on Queen Square:

> This machine is no more than a common pump whose pestern [sic] is made to work perpendicularly thro' a cap fixed to the head of the barrel, with an air vessel by the side of the pump, and some other small things. By the turn of a cock, one of these pumps discharges the water, as by a lifting or forcing quality; and I have one of them in a well belonging to my own house in Queen-Square in Bath, which becomes an engine in a second of time; so that if a fire should break out within forty or fifty yards of it, the water in the well may be instantly raised up, conducted by a leather-pipe, and forced out to stop its progress.[35]

So inextricably linked were these two entrepreneurs that in 1728 Wood went with Allen to pitch for the contract to supply stone for the Greenwich Hospital project. As the project already had an architect and surveyor, Wood's role in Greenwich was, therefore, to help Allen by providing the technical information. During the building of Prior Park, Allen retained Wood for five years so that he could provide any prospective builders wanting to use Bath stone with estimates and advice:

> By the great resort of strangers to Bath, the Fame of Mr Allen's Stone Works was soon carried to the principal parts of the Kingdom and letters came to him in great abundance, some with draughts requiring the value of executing them in Free Stone, and some without draughts with a request to know what would be proper for such and such purposes. To enable him to answer all such letters, together with personal applications to the same effect, he proposed to allow me a certain sum per annum in consideration of my giving him proper instructions, which he accordingly had from me during the course of the next five years.[36]

Allen obviously did not possess the type of specialist expertise required. He was reliant on Wood, or if Wood was unavailable on Omer or Biggs.

In Greenwich they were up against the popular and favoured Portland stone. Bath stone was thought to be too soft. Although they failed to win the contract, Wood believed he had won the argument, as, according to him, Colen Campbell had been unable to tell the

---

34 For example Henry Fielding's *Miscellanies* of 1743.

35 Wood, *Exchange*, 1745, pp.18-19.

36 Wood, *Essay*, p.433.

34 difference between Portland and Bath stone. There was, Wood noted, great opposition to the introduction of Bath freestone into London, 'some of the opponents maliciously comparing it to Cheshire Cheese, liable to breed Maggots that would soon devour it'.[37]

Soon after this disappointment, Wood recorded that, in 1728, he and Allen started to work on designs for a mansion that would show Bath stone 'to much greater advantage', although building on the site at Prior Park did not start until 1734.[38] Prior Park was conceived with much ornamentation inside and outside to show the value, beauty and ease of working Bath stone [fig. 20]. But Prior Park also demonstrates the expertise of the architect and the contracted masons. The building that Wood designed responded to the site and

Fig. 20

contour of the landscape, but ironically related to Campbell's unrealised plan for Wanstead House, Essex. Wood undertook to surpass Campbell, whom he said had 'boasted of the justness of [his] Hexastyle Porticoe'.[39]

It was during the building of Prior Park that historians have conjectured that Allen and Wood quarrelled. Wood only built the basement storey and was then replaced by Jones. As we have seen this was not a departure for Allen, who had taken Wood's design for his house in Lilliput Alley, but had given the building contract to another. Both Allen and Wood are well known to have quarrelled with a number of their friends, collaborators and patrons. Wood fell out with Robert Gay and Lord Chandos, both of whom continued to do business with him. Allen famously snubbed Alexander Pope after eight years of close friendship. It may even have been Pope's interference at Prior Park that drove a wedge between Wood and Allen.[40] There was further conflict between the two during the building of the Parades, but as we have seen they went on to collaborate successfully on the Bristol Exchange and the General Hospital.

The absence of any reference to Allen in Wood's first edition of the *Essay* has also been read as evidence of a quarrel, and it should

---

37 Wood, *Essay*, p.426.
38 Wood, *Essay*, p.427.
39 Wood, *Essay*, p.432.
40 Pope quickly offered his services to Allen as a consultant on the interior decoration and the landscaping of the estate. In less than a month of being told of Allen's plan to build Prior Park, Pope had obtained permission from art collectors to have their paintings copied by the artist Johan Van Diest for four large paintings to ornament the (yet unbuilt) central hall. 'A man not only shews his taste but his virtue, in the choice of such ornaments.' Pope, *Correspondence*. IV, April 1736, p.13. In *Essay* Wood complained that in 1749 the delicate stone decoration of the interior was cut-off and replaced with wood panelling.

be noted that despite Allen's prominence in the Corporation and his election as Mayor in 1742, Wood never won a public contract in Bath. The reason for Allen's absence can only be a matter for speculation. Begun in 1740, Wood's most ambitious architectural plan, The Royal Forum (with its surrounding Parades) [Cat. Nos. 35 & 36], was, frankly, ruined by Allen. As a sub-leaseholder Allen strove to cut the costs he and fellow lessees, John Taylor and George Lockup, had to endure. Wood noted that the 'Scheme, contrived by one of the Tenants...to lay aside the Ornaments; to alter the Proportion of the Walk; and to erect the Terrass Wall with Rubble Stone' had been 'in Violation of the Articles' and had led 'to the Destruction of a Design, which, on Paper, hath given Pleasure and Satisfaction to Multitudes, among all Ranks of People'.[41]

The Parades are now a rather ignoble feature of Bath's cityscape. Few visitors admire this scheme as they do Wood's other achievements. It was, and still is, a damning shame that Wood's dream for this part of Bath was unrealised.[42] Perhaps, unlike the visionary Wood, Allen's benevolent capitalism was more purely driven by economy and profit.

Wood also chastised the Corporation vehemently in the first edition of *Essay*, mainly due to what he saw as its narrow-minded attitude and corruption.[43] The expanded second edition, printed seven years later, incorporates numerous references to Allen, praising both the houses he owned and his management of the quarries. Perhaps Wood did not want to associate the newly elected Mayor and his friend with this past dishonesty.

The friendship and collaboration between Wood and Allen benefited both men. It was based on a love of the natural oolitic limestone, on humanitarian acts, on learning, on enterprise and on the promotion of Bath. Wood's *Essay* shines out as a testament to these glories. Any fashionable reader of fashionable society would have undoubtedly felt compelled to visit Bath for the season, or perhaps even move to the city. This powerful advertisement would have pleased all men involved with Bath's commerciality, no one more so than the quarry owner and Mayor, Ralph Allen.

41 *Essay*, p.350.
42 For further discussion of Wood's Royal Forum refer to the essays by Mowl and Frost in this volume and catalogue number 37.
43 The Corporation refused to improve the approach to the Queen's Bath and a former mayor had reputedly refused to enlarge the Pump Room as it would have impinged on his son's coffee-house business.

The vision of John Wood: Bath as an imaginary city
Amy Frost

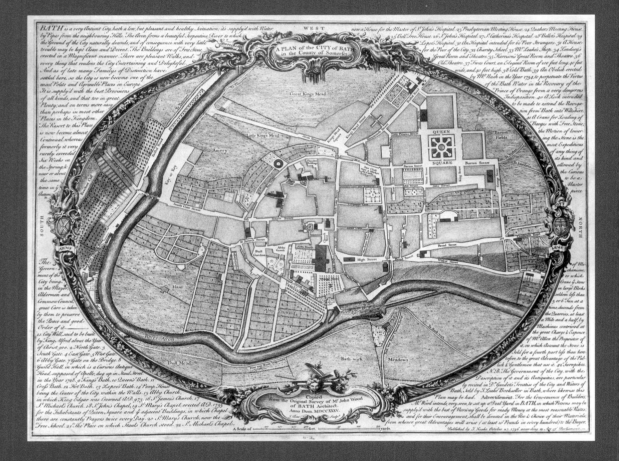

Fig. 21
*A plan of the City of Bath copied
from the Original Survey of Mr
John Wood of Bath, Architect,
printed by James Leake, 1736*

In *The Origin of Building* John Wood the Elder quoted what Vitruvius had deemed the necessary qualities of an architect and then stated that they were only possible when given to a man, such as Moses or Solomon, by God:

> *Architecture consists of such Variety of Knowledge, that before a Man can justly assume the Title of an Architect, he must be able to Write and Design, be skill'd in Geometry, and not ignorant of Opticks, that he must be acquainted with Arithmatick and Musick, be very knowing in History and Philosophy, and have some Tincture of Physick, Law and Astrology...these are Qualifications not attainable at once by our own Abilities.*[1]

Wood was a man whose mind was constantly in motion, filling his thoughts with new ideas, educating himself with different theories and facts, adapting his ideas accordingly and ultimately producing the outpouring of these ideas in stone. In his attempts to master history, geometry, astronomy and mathematics he was perhaps striving to be a true architect and come as close to Vitruvius's ideal as was possible for a mortal man. This may be a grand and, for Wood, unattainable ambition, but grand ideas were what he excelled at. It is through investigating just how far he pushed his imagination that a clearer picture of Wood can be revealed, although perhaps not according to his ideal of a true architect, but rather our image of a visionary one.

Just as the Bath John Wood returned to in 1727 was the remains of a glorious ancient city, Georgian Bath that we know today is the residue of an ideal city which was never built. What Wood actually constructed is a mere fragment, a small aspect of the much larger and monumental image that he imagined.

In his *Essay Towards a Description of Bath*, Wood informs his reader that in 1725, at the age of 21, he asked for a plan of Bath to be sent to him while working in Yorkshire. He studied the form of Bath, the residue of the ancient city still sitting within the medieval walls, and claimed that, 'I began to turn my thoughts towards the improvement of the City by Building.'[2]

He goes on to state where in the city his building will take place, and what it will include. Wood proposed to construct not simply individual structures, but entire spaces that would redefine

---

1   John Wood, *The Origin of Building, or the Plagiarism of the Heathens Detected*, 1741. Second Book, Chapter 1, p.68.
2   John Wood, *An Essay Towards a Description of Bath* (2nd ed., 1749). Vol I, Part II, p.232.

38

not only the appearance, but also the entire shape and size of the city. In today's terms, Wood envisaged a regeneration scheme and produced a masterplan for the city of Bath made up of three main components:

> I proposed to make a grand place of Assembly, to be called the Royal Forum of Bath; another place, no less magnificent, for the Exhibition of Sport, to be called the Grand Circus; and a third place, of equal state with either of the former, for the Practise of medicinal exercises, to be called the Imperial Gymnasium of the city.[3]

In 1735, ten years after his vision for Bath was conjured up, Wood published a map of the city, as if to illustrate his progress and indicate the areas upon which he had decided his masterplan would be realised [fig. 21, p.36]. Queen Square is immediately recognisable and the plan of its central garden is the most prominent feature on the map, overshadowing even Bath Abbey. This map is Wood illustrating what he has achieved, perhaps in an attempt to persuade further landowners and investors to back his plans. Unlike the majority of maps of Bath, which read south-north, Wood's map is orientated east-west. This is undoubtedly intentional, as it means the bottom left of the map is entirely made up of Abbey Orchard and the Ham, the areas of undeveloped land on which Wood planned to construct firstly his Grand Circus, and then his Royal Forum.

It is not known whether Wood ever produced a drawing of his masterplan for Bath. There are no surviving projected maps or detailed plans. While only fragments were completed, the whole remains unrealised. However, because his plan was not built it does not mean that it did not exist. Some designs are made to be realised on paper only, while others will remain forever just a vision in the mind's eye. The realm of the architectural drawing is often more interesting than the built product, as it is a realm in which the imagination has no restraints, a world in which anything is possible, and all buildings are realisable. Using what few drawings by Wood that survive, alongside his published account of his work in the *Essay*, it is possible to unravel some of the mysteries behind his grand scheme for the city.

The Imperial Gymnasium was an 18th century spa complex.

3   Ibid.

Wood wanted to restore the King's and Queen's Baths, enlarge the Pump Room to make it more accommodating to the increasing numbers of visitors to the city, and to construct a new general hospital. What kind of structure or space Wood planned to build in order to link all these individual components together is unknown. The Imperial Gymnasium remains just an ambition, an unrealised dream of which the Bath Mineral Water Hospital is merely a residue. Yet if the plans for it had survived, or indeed if Wood ever actually got so far as to draw up plans for this complex, they would have been extraordinary.

The only insights into the Royal Forum, both written and visual, can be found in the rare Third Volume of *An Essay Towards a Description of Bath*.[4] Compared to the ground plans of Queen Square and the proposed St James' Triangle gardens on Abbey Orchard published in Volumes One and Two, the plan for the Forum is an extremely basic image [fig. 22]. It has the appearance not of a finished

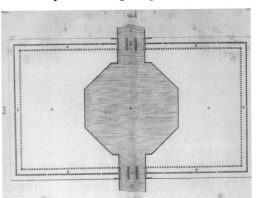

Fig. 22

final design, but of a work in progress. It is not like the well-rendered engravings that can be found in the first two volumes of the *Essay*. This suggests that perhaps this rare third volume of Wood's work is the only known copy, for the simple reason that it is actually the only copy ever produced. The Forum plan is not of the standard one expects from an engraving by Pierre Fourdrinier published in a John Wood book. It does not have a scale bar, something that Wood never fails to include in his published designs. Three illustrations for Wood's Bristol Exchange, believed to be proof plates sent to Wood by his engraver for amendments, clearly show the architect adding scale bars to the illustrations [see Cat. Nos. 30-32]. Perhaps this third volume is itself a proof copy that was never actually

4   1743. The original is preserved in Bath Central Library.

40

published. It is hard to believe that Wood did not provide a scale bar on the plan of the Royal Forum as it would be the best way to illustrate the size of the space, and in so doing the magnitude of what he was proposing.

A further clue to the appearance of the Forum comes from the largest known collection of drawings by Wood, which includes several designs for a bridge [fig. 23].[5] With three supports and a continuous balustrade, the bridge would fit perfectly into both the description of the Forum and the representation of the bridges on the Forum ground plan.

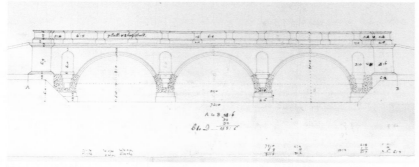

Fig. 23

While the Imperial Gymnasium only existed in Wood's mind and the Royal Forum existed on paper, the only element of the masterplan to be completed – the Grand Circus – is, ironically, the most mysterious of them all. There are no known drawings by either John Wood the Elder or his son for the façades of the Circus. The elder Wood died only three months after the foundation stone was laid, and never got to see his dream fulfilled. Had Wood lived longer he would have undoubtedly revised *An Essay Towards a Description of Bath* to include a discussion of the Circus, revealing some of its secrets that continue to challenge the viewer today. The work was completed by the younger Wood and the lack of any drawings by either architect has always led to speculation over how much of the design of the Circus each man was responsible for. Wood's failing health saw him increasingly delegating projects to his son, so that by the time the designs for the Circus were under discussion in the late 1740s, the working relationship between the

5   See Cat. No. 26.

two men had strongly evolved.

Once again it is through drawings that both the relationship of the two Woods and further evidence of the elder Wood's architectural development can be revealed. The book of drawings held at Bath Central Library, in which the Forum bridge designs can be found, also includes several designs worked on by both the elder and younger Wood. Most notably there are a series of plans and elevations for a country villa flanked by two small pavilions (fig. 24). These are drawings for Buckland House, built in Berkshire by the younger Wood for Robert Throckmorton in 1757.[6] Completed just two years after the elder Wood's death, these drawings clearly show both men working on the designs for the building.

Fig. 24

The book also contains several designs for small, unbuilt houses, the majority of which follow a similar regular composition. However, the most intriguing set are plans and elevations for a part-castellated building worked on by both father and son.[7] These drawings offer an insight into Wood the Elder's mind as it is the only time he is seen to be designing in a style different from the Palladianism he employed in Bath. The elevations vary from basic five-bay designs with only a battlemented roofline and porch

Fig. 25

displaying elements of the Gothic, to the same five-bay façade with corner towers that are strangely at odds with the repeated Venetian windows complete with triangular pediments [fig. 25]. One elevation even has towers attached to the

6   Folios 7-22 of the book of drawings, see Cat. No. 26. For Buckland see C Hussey, *The English Country House – Early Georgian 1715-1760*, 1955, pp.204-7.

7   Folios 69-74.

42

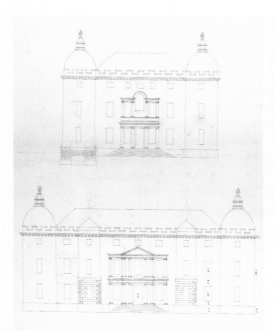

Fig. 26

façade, the projections and recessions creating the sort of movement associated with the Baroque [fig. 26]. As a Gothic design it is a half-hearted attempt, classicised by the application of a two-storey entrance portico.[8] The mix of classical and castellated features sit unhappily together, and it has been suggested that these drawings are for the renovation of an existing house by Wood, in which he is attempting to apply his Palladianism to an older façade.[9] Whether this was the case remains a matter for conjecture. However, what is vital is that these drawings are unlike anything that the elder Wood ever built or even projected again.[10] We are presented with the existence on paper of another aspect of Wood's architectural development, an imaginary castle that offers an insight into his drawing style, his partnership with his son, a tentative attempt at Gothic and a further demonstration of his devotion to classicism.

Wood's draughtsmanship of initial designs in the book is basic with little detailed rendering compared to the drawings prepared for publication, such as those for Prior Park that are also in the book and are eventually published in the *Essay*.[11] His drawings show initial ideas amended with hastily added sketches. They pose the question: what would John Wood's masterplan for Bath have looked like? Would it have been a collection of individual designs, plans and maps or a single view, a *capriccio* encompassing the entire city?

8   This two-storey portico with prominent pairs of attached columns alongside the elevations with a series of windows flanked by paired columns is perhaps the closest drawing that exists to the relationship of windows and columns that Wood eventually creates on the façade of the Circus. Drawn at some point in the 1740s it shows him experimenting with these elements.

9   Timothy Mowl believes this house to be Kelston Park, near Bath, see Timothy Mowl & Brian Earnshaw, *John Wood: Architect of Obsession* (Bath, 1988), Chapter 11.

On Friday, 23 July 2004 *Building Design* ran the headline 'End of the Iconic Age?' It introduced a front-page article discussing the fading out of the 'signature' building epitomised by Frank Gehry's Guggenheim Museum in Bilbao. The signature building once represented the key to regeneration projects attempting to rejuvenate failing towns and cities. The article stated that the situation is now changing. It is not enough to design a single structure in the hope that the environment around it will be redeveloped following its success. The end of the signature building heralds the rise of the masterplanner and provides the perfect blank page for fantasists and visionaries. Regeneration is now seen as taking whole spaces and re-defining them, re-carving and restoring the landscape of the town or city – just as John Wood did over 250 years ago.

The future of building in Bath is intrinsically linked to Wood's vision, but not as generally assumed. Rather than use the aesthetic of Wood's buildings as patterns for neo-Georgian buildings that lack the conviction of theory or philosophy to support them, it is the visionary nature of Wood's work that Bath needs to address. The Bath Spa building, designed by Nicholas Grimshaw & Partners, heralds a new age in Bath architecture, when the imagination, and more importantly, the confidence of the city shall be put to the test [fig. 27].

Fig. 27

---

10 The younger Wood actually did build a Gothic house, Tregenna Castle near St Ives in Cornwall, now a hotel. The only indication of Gothic is in the basic crenellated roofline. It is, however, very similar in appearance to the designs in the book of drawings, showing that the younger Wood was clearly influenced by the castle designs he had worked on with his father.

11 Folios 48-57 of the *Book of Drawings* are designs for Prior Park.

Fig. 28

Fig. 29

At present the future vision for Bath's architecture exists, as much of Wood's work does, on paper only. The southern part of the city centre consists of a shopping complex and bus station constructed during the 1970s, that has, like so many structures from that period, failed to live up to its long-term potential and has aged badly. The site is now due for redevelopment and proposals have been presented as an idealised *capriccio* [fig. 28]. More striking are the Wilkinson Eyre Architects designs for an integrated Transport Interchange, the vital element of this area's regeneration [fig. 29]. Still in the initial stages of development, the most important point about these views and drawings is their ability to force the public into considering the potential of new architecture in the city, and encourage them to consider new possibilities.

Architectural drawing in the current age inhabits the domain of computer technology, yet the architect's vision, the excitement and passion of a raw initial idea, remains best conveyed through the hastily drawn sketch.[12] The sense of urgency is soon displaced or filtered out through the process of translating initial ideas into computer programmes. A similar situation occurred in the 18th century, when the urgency of a design would be filtered out as a drawing that was reproduced as an engraving, print or as an illustration in a book.[13] It is interesting then that at present the best illustrations of the largest development the city will have seen since Wood's architecture sparked off the building boom of the 18th century are a series of sketches (fig. 30). The Bath Western Riverside is a 28-hectare site stretching out from the city centre to its western

12 In 1998 the V&A Museum held an exhibition *On the back of an Envelope*, discussing the importance of the initial sketch to the design process.

13 With the exception of Piranesi's engravings where, despite the time consuming and exact nature of the engraving process, the passion and excitement of one of the greatest architectural fantasists can be seen in every line.

fringes. Made up of three separate areas, it is a project that will see each component of land linked together and in turn the whole site linked to the city. It is reminiscent of Wood's vision of linking the three elements of his masterplan for Bath. It will include a cultural centre, commercial and entertainment areas as well as new housing. It is not just a regeneration scheme, it is a blank canvas on which the future of Bath architecture will be realised.

In the publication accompanying the RIBA/Hayward Gallery 2004 touring exhibition *Fantasy Architecture*, Archigram's Peter Cook, whose most significant visions for ideal cities remain on paper only, sums up the situation of building in a city such as Bath:

> The so-called 'fantastic' architect is just the one who has pushed a little bit further than the 'Ordinary' architect. Good buildings are pretty 'fantastic' because they are so rare. Many 'fantastic' buildings should have been built.[14]

In order to ensure that 'good' buildings are constructed in the city, Bath needs now to consider the idea of pushing the limits of both architects' and viewers' imagination just that little bit harder. It is, after all, a city built upon the imagination of an architect, and so it should continue to be in the future. Will the architects and masterplanners of Bath continue what John Wood started and proclaim the magnificence of this city through its architecture?

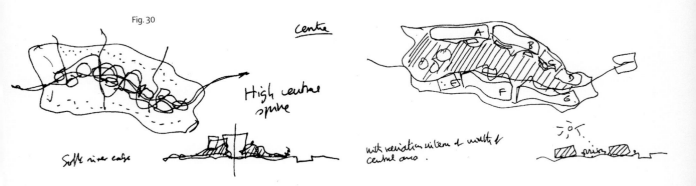

Fig. 30

14 Peter Cook, 'The Drawing as Wish', *Fantasy Architecture*, Hayward Gallery, 2004, p.26.

Catalogue

1. The mystery years

'…the Name of WOOD, the Restorer of Bath, will always be sacred here.'

Bath Journal, 18 February 1754

48

The early years of John Wood's life are something of a mystery. He was baptised in Bath on 24 August 1704, but the exact details of his education, activities and movements in the years following remain unknown. At some point he must have left Bath and in 1721, at the age of 17, he was in London, leasing land and building townhouses.

The mystery is made more intriguing as Wood, this young son of a builder from the provinces, managed to get himself admitted into the circle of some of England's most influential gentlemen of wealth and taste.

In London Wood found himself surrounded by the developments and innovations of British Neo-Classical architecture. By 1724 he was also working at Bramham Park in Yorkshire, which provided him with experience in the great tradition of English country house building to complement the knowledge he had acquired in the City.

It was during this period of practical education that John Wood began to experiment with an architectural style that became his first great obsession: Palladianism.

1   Joseph Gilmore. See page 4

2   *Vitruvius Britannicus,* **Vol. II**
Colen Campbell
Published 1717
520 x 370mm
University of Bath Library
67-333 77

Plate 82 illustrating Bramham Park, Yorkshire, the country seat of Robert Benson, 1st Lord Bingley

Bramham Park was built between 1699-1710 and is a relatively typical example of the English Baroque. The house has been attributed to both James Gibbs and Thomas Archer, and while either or both of these architects could have worked on ideas for the building, it is most likely that the final design was made by Robert Benson himself, who was known to be a highly skilled amateur architect.

For *Vitruvius Britannicus* see Cat. No. 5

2

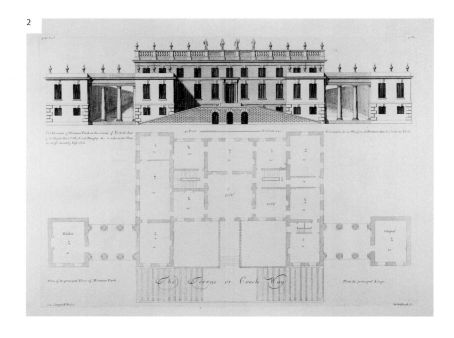

John Wood in Yorkshire

Wood met Robert Benson, 1st Lord Bingley and the builder of Bramham Park, while working in London. Benson, famed for his skill as an amateur architect, employed Wood at Bramham between 1724-27, and it was at the Yorkshire estate that Wood's architectural education continued.

As well as the map of the estate indicating the canal and alterations to the parkland for which Wood was responsible, the main contribution of the Bath architect at the country estate was the Stable Block. The central body of this building, with its four-columned portico and cupola, is Wood's first truly Palladian work. Although it is a relatively unremarkable design by an inexperienced architect, it marks the beginning of John Wood's obsession with the style that was dominating British architecture, and which he would develop further in Bath.

Fig. 31
A design for a stable block by John Wood the Elder (possibly for Prior Park)

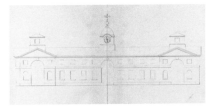

Fig. 32
The aqueduct designed by John Wood the Elder for Bramham Park, Yorkshire

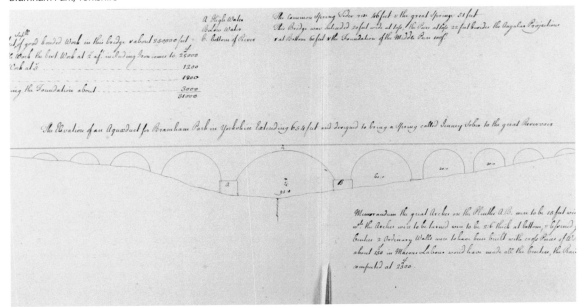

2. The rise of Palladianism

'Architecture is a term under which is comprehended all the causes and rules of Building'

John Wood, *The Origin of Building*

52

The only written work to describe the orders of architecture that survived from classical antiquity was *De Architectura* by the Roman architect, Vitruvius. However, by the 15th century, architects had begun to initiate a tradition for developing theories on the principles and origins of building through the publication of architectural books or treatises.

In 1570 the Renaissance architect, Andrea Palladio, published the most famous treatise on building: *I Quattro libri dell'architettura* (the Four Books on Architecture). Palladio defined the rules and proportions of architecture and showed how they could be used correctly by illustrating buildings of his own design alongside those that had survived from antiquity.

The practical and theoretical influence of Palladio on English architecture was immense. In the early 17th century the architect Inigo Jones studied Palladio's buildings and writings and began designing in a clean, simple and elegant classical style. He became the first great English reviver of Palladio and his work continues to be regarded as the most truthful example of English Palladianism.

In 1715 the Neo-Palladian style began to dominate English architecture. Publications on how to build, what to build and how to decorate flooded the libraries of architects and amateurs alike. John Wood read, had access to and purchased such books, and they illustrate the architectural climate in England at the time he conceived his vision for Bath.

3

3   *Inigo Jones*
     A Bannerman after Van Dyck
     Date unknown
     Engraving
     335 x 240mm
     Building of Bath Museum
     PR/7

Inigo Jones (1573-1652) is the father of English Palladianism. His career began as a designer of Masques for the Royal Court, but it was as an architect to the Stuart kings that Jones found his fame.

In 1615 Jones became Surveyor General of the King's Office of Works. A year later he designed the Queen's House, Greenwich, widely considered to be England's first great Palladian Revival building.

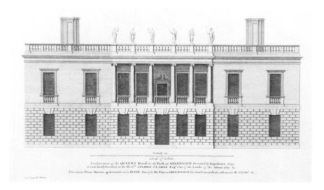

Fig. 33
The Queen's House, Greenwich (1616-35), designed by Inigo Jones, *Vitruvius Britannicus*, Vol. I

The importance of 1715

100 years after Inigo Jones was made Surveyor General of the King's Works (the body responsible for the design of major public buildings), the progression of English Palladianism was catapulted forward by the publication in 1715 of two very important works: the first complete English translation of Palladio's *I Quattro libri dell'architettura*, translated by Giacomo Leoni, and the publication of the first volume of Colen Campbell's *Vitruvius Britannicus*.

4 **I Quatrro libri dell'architettura**
   Andrea Palladio
   First published 1570
   465 x 300 x 50mm
   This version published 1715
   Translation by Giacomo Leoni
   Book, printed by John Watts, London
   Special Collections, Information Services, University of Bristol Library

Although Palladio's work had been available to English architects in Italian since its publication in 1570, Leoni's publication was particularly important: for the very first time all Four Books were now available in the English language. This enabled more architects, builders and enthusiasts to study the rules of architecture as defined by Palladio.

Leoni's translation of the *Quattro libri* was re-printed several times and John Wood owned a copy of the 1740 edition.

E Harris & N Savage, 'Palladio', *British Architectural Books and Writers 1556-1785*, Cambridge University Press, Cambridge, 1990, pp.348-365. R Tavernor, *Palladio & Palladianism*, Thames & Hudson, 1991.

4

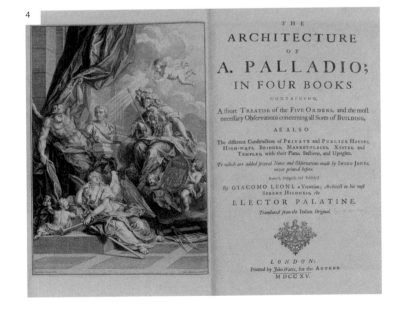

THE
ARCHITECTURE
OF
A. PALLADIO;
IN FOUR BOOKS

CONTAINING,

A short TREATISE of the FIVE ORDERS, and the most necessary Observations concerning all Sorts of BUILDING,

AS ALSO

The different Construction of PRIVATE and PUBLICK HOUSES, HIGH-WAYS, BRIDGES, MARKET-PLACES, XYSTES, and TEMPLES, with their Plans, Sections, and Uprights.

To which are added several Notes and Observations made by INIGO JONES, never printed before.

Revis'd, Design'd, and Publish'd

By GIACOMO LEONI, a Venetian; Architect to his most SERENE HIGHNESS, the

ELECTOR PALATINE.

Translated from the Italian Original.

LONDON:
Printed by *John Watts*, for the AUTHOR.
MDCCXV.

5

The West Front of Wansted in Essex the Seat of Sr Richard Child Baronet Hereditary Warden of Waltham Forest &c.
Co: Campbell Inv: et Delin.   To whom this Plate is most humbly Inscrib'd

a Scale of 40 Feet

Elevation de L'Entreé du Chateau de WANSTED dans la Comté D'ESSEX appartenant a M.r CHILD Chevalier.

Extendi 160.

56

By the time the third volume of *Vitruvius Britannicus* was published in 1725, Colen Campbell's designs for neo-Palladian mansions had become models for the country house building boom of the 18th century. However, his position at the front of the style was soon surpassed. A new figurehead for British Palladianism had emerged in the form of the rich, educated and influential Richard Boyle, 3rd Earl of Burlington.

At his townhouse in London and his self-designed villa at Chiswick, Burlington collected around him a group of talented artists, sculptors and architects, who sought to create a pure and noble architectural style for England. Included in this so-called 'Circle of Taste' was William Kent, with whom the architect Earl formed a strong aesthetic partnership.

The influence of Burlington and Kent's partnership was far reaching. With *Vitruvius Britannicus* as a pattern book on how to build a country house, and members of Burlington's circle firmly placed in the King's Office of Works, English Neo-Palladianism dominated the style of both large private homes and significant public buildings, defining English architecture in the 18th century.

Previous page

5 *Vitruvius Britannicus,* Vol. I
Colen Campbell
Published 1715
Printed book
520 x 370mm
University of Bath Library
67-333 76

Initially intended to be a catalogue of English country houses, *Vitruvius Britannicus* became the pattern book for English neo-Palladianisim. By placing 17th-century architecture against the work of Inigo Jones, Campbell contrasted the excesses of the Baroque, with the clean purity of Jones. He then included designs of his own invention, such as this one for Wanstead House, as a way of stating what modern buildings in England should look like.

The full title of this work is *Virtuvius Britannicus or the British Architect;* the architect in question is Inigo Jones, here heralded as the hero and benchmark to which all English architects should aspire.

TP Connor, *'The Making of Vitruvius Britannicus',* Architectural History, XX, 1977, pp.14-30. E Harris & N Savage, 'Colen Campbell', *British Architectural Books and Writers 1556-1785,* Cambridge University Press, Cambridge, 1990, pp.139-148. N Savage, 'Colen Campbell 1676-1729', *Mark J Millard Architectural Collection,* Vol. II, British Books 17th-18th Centuries, National Gallery of Art, Washington, 1998, pp.45-63.

Fig. 34
Stourhead House, Wiltshire
(1720-24), designed by
Colen Campbell, *Vitruvius Britannicus,* Vol. II

6 *A Book of Architecture, Containing Designs of Buildings and Ornaments* **James Gibbs** Published 1728 Book, printed in London 390 x 540 x 55mm Special Collections, Information Services, University of Bristol Library Gift of Bryan Little

The work of James Gibbs is noticeably absent from *Vitruvius Britannicus*. Gibbs reacted to such neglect by publishing a treatise on architecture comprised entirely of his own designs. It was the first of its kind by an English architect, and its influence stretched as far as America. The most famous building to be inspired by the work of Gibbs is the White House in Washington DC.

This copy is especially interesting as it is inscribed 'Margaret Cavendish Harley Feb 1731-2'. This is the daughter and heir of Edward, Lord Harley, one of the country's greatest collectors of books. As well as being Gibbs' main patron, Harley was also the man on whose London estate John Wood first began his architectural career. Gibbs' *Book of Architecture* is known to have been in the collection of John Wood the Younger, and was most probably handed down from father to son.

E Harris & N Savage 'James Gibbs', *British Architectural Books and Writers 1556-1785*, Cambridge University Press, Cambridge, 1990, pp.208-213.

6

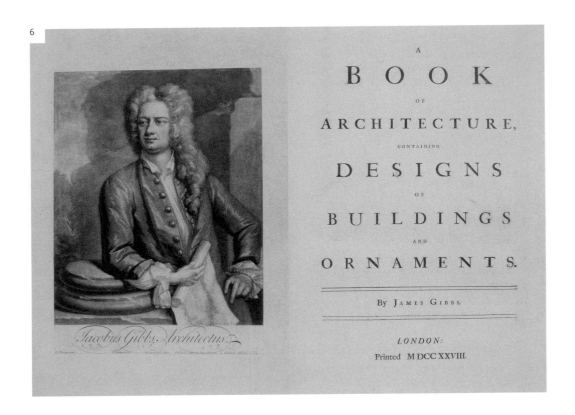

58   7   *I Quattro libri dell'architettura*
Andrea Palladio
First published in Italian 1570
Translated and edited by
Isaac Ware
Published by the patronage
of Lord Burlington, 1737
Printed book
400 x 250 x 40mm
Building of Bath Museum
1994:ill

This edition of Palladio's *Quattro libri dell'architettura* by the architect Isaac Ware is considered the most accurate English translation because the initial text was read and revised by Lord Burlington.

As a member of Burlington's circle, Ware had access to the Earl's extensive architectural library, which included the copy of the *Quattro libri* owned by Inigo Jones. Book One was published by Ware in 1737, with the subsequent three Books following over the next five years. In 1742 the complete work was published and subscribed to by John Wood the Elder.

E Harris & N Savage, 'Isaac Ware', *British Architectural Books and Writers 1556-1785*, Cambridge University Press, Cambridge, 1990, pp.468-476. For Palladio see Cat. No. 4.

7

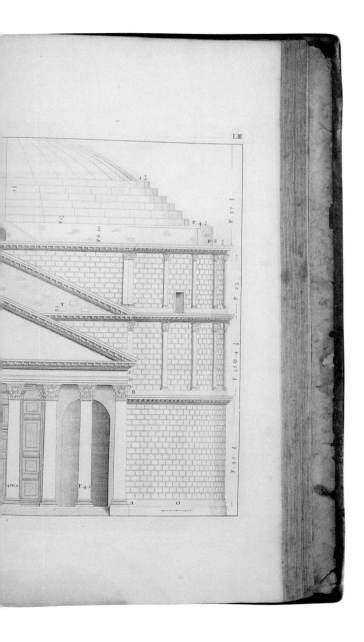

8

THE
BUILDER's JEWEL:
OR, THE
YOUTH's INSTRUCTOR,
AND
WORKMAN's REMEMBRANCER.
EXPLAINING
Short and Easy RULES,
Made familiar to the meaneſt Capacity,
For DRAWING and WORKING,
I. The FIVE ORDERS of Columns entire; or any Part of
an Order, without Regard to the Module or Diameter.
And to enrich them
With their Ruſticks, Flutings, Cablings, Dentules, Modillions, &c.
Alſo to proportion
Their Doors, Windows, Intercolumnations, Portico's, and Arcades.
TOGETHER WITH
Fourteen Varieties of Raking, Circular, Scrolled, Compound, and Contracted
Pediments; and the true Formation and Accædering of their Raking and Re-
turned Cornices; and Mouldings for Capping their Dentules and Modillions.
II. Block and Cantaliver Cornices. Ruſtick Quoins, Cornices propor-
tioned to Rooms, Angle Brackets, Mouldings for Tabernacle Frames, Pannelling,
and Centering for Groins, Truſſed Partitions, Gantry, Roofs and Domes.
With a Section of the Dome of St. Paul's, LONDON.
The Whole Illuſtrated by upwards of 200 Examples, engraved on 100 Copper-Plates.
By B. and T. LANGLEY.
LONDON,
Printed for R. WARE, at the Bible and Sun, on Ludgate-Hill. M.DCC.LVII.
(Price 4s. 6d.)

8   *The Builder's Jewel*
Batty Langley
Book, printed by R Ware at the
Bible and Sun on Ludgate Hill
Published 1757
150 x 115 x 25mm
Special Collections, Information
Services, University of Bristol
Library

With no apparent official training
or experience of building, Batty
Langley was responsible for a
huge outpouring of publications
on architecture.

His works covered all aspects of
the building trade; their small size
made them highly practical and
accessible to a wide readership of
builders, masons, surveyors and
all forms of craftsman. A defiant
member of the anti-Burlington
circle, Langley was a constant
defender of Gothic architecture,
and even invented five Gothic
orders. Langley is also one of the
most famous architectural
authors known to be a dedicated
Freemason.

E Harris & N Savage, 'Batty Langley', *British
Architectural Books and Writers 1556-1785*,
Cambridge University Press, Cambridge, 1990,
pp.262-280.

9

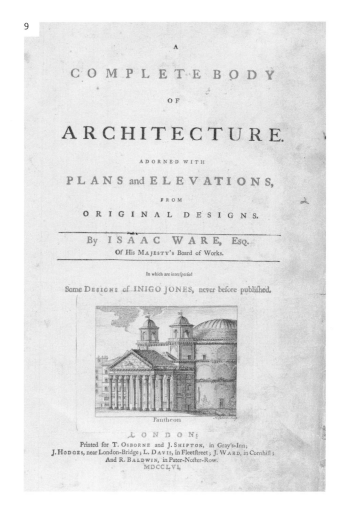

9   *A Complete Body of Architecture*
Isaac Ware
Published 1757
Book, printed by T Osbourne &
J Shipton, London
405 x 265 x 70mm
Building of Bath Museum
1993:19

Ware's *Body of Architecture*
was published in individual
instalments between 1755-57
with the intent that these parts
be bound together into a single
volume. It is a practical work,
taking the reader step-by-step
through different building
methods and materials.

Despite the usefulness of its
contents, the sheer size and
weight of the book made it far
less practical than the small
works produced by Batty Langley
in the 1740s.

For Ware see Cat. No. 7.

10 **A Treatise on Civil Architecture**
William Chambers
Published 1768, 2nd edition
Book, printed by J Dixwell,
London
554 x 380 x 38mm
Building of Bath Museum
1993:17

William Chambers, famous for
being the architectural tutor of
the young Prince of Wales, later
George III, published the first
edition of this work in 1759. It
was well received in both England
and France, where Chambers had
studied architecture under the
tutorship of Blondel.

Unlike Isaac Ware's *Body of
Architecture,* Chambers' *Treatise*
concentrates on the theoretical
origin and development of
building and ornamentation.
During 1770-71 Chambers began
preparing a series of 'Discourses
on Architecture' to be delivered
to the Royal Academy. Although
never published, elements of
these lectures were included in
the revised 3rd edition of the
Treatise published in 1791.

E Harris *Treatise on Civil Architecture,* Sir William
Chambers: *Knight of the Polar Star,* J Harris,
A Zwemmer Ltd., 1970, pp.108-27; with
N Savage 'William Chambers', *British
Architectural Books and Writers 1556-1785,*
Cambridge University Press, Cambridge,
1990, pp.155-164.

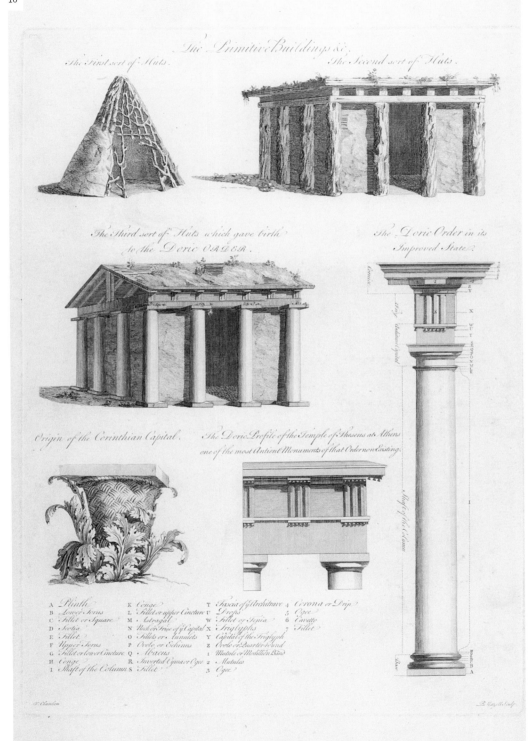

The Primitive Buildings &c.

The First sort of Huts.

The Second sort of Huts.

The Third sort of Huts which gave birth to the Doric ORDER.

The Doric Order in its Improved State.

Origin of the Corinthian Capital.

The Doric Profile of the Temple of Theseus at Athens one of the most Antient Monuments of that Order now Existing.

A	Plinth	K	Conge	T	Fascia of y Architrave	4 Corona or Drip
B	Lower Torus	L	Fillet or upper Cincture	V	Drops	5 Ogee
C	Fillet or Square	M	Astragal	W	Fillet or Tenia	6 Cavetto
D	Scotia	N	Neck or Frise of y Capital	X	Triglyphs	7 Fillet
E	Fillet	O	Fillets or Annulets	Y	Capital of the Triglyph	
F	Upper Torus	P	Ovolo or Echinus	Z	Ovolo or Quarter round	
G	Fillet or lower Cincture	Q	Abacus	1	Mutule or Modillion Band	
H	Conge	R	Inverted Cyma or Ogee	2	Mutules	
I	Shaft of the Column	S	Fillet	3	Ogee	

Chambers

B. Roy M. Culp.

3. John Wood's theories on architecture

'In this Temple, a man might have seen all that Art was capable of producing'

John Wood, *The Origin of Building*

64

Amidst the influx of architects defining their beliefs through books, John Wood published a theory on the origin and development of architecture that stands apart from most of his contemporaries. Strange, eccentric and very personal, Wood altered facts, twisted truths and adapted history in order to prove his own ideas.

Tracing the origin of the architectural orders back to biblical times, Wood manipulated the God-given dimensions of Noah's Ark, Moses' Tabernacle, and the Temple of Solomon to claim the importance and, ultimately, Christian provenance of the monuments of ancient Britain.

It is an ideology in which mystery, myth and legend become tools to illustrate how the buildings of classical antiquity were merely imitations of those developed in the Holy Land, and how England's architectural roots can be found in Jerusalem.

According to Wood, the entire history of architecture hinges on the presence of one individual – King Bladud. Wood believed that Bladud's heroic and sometimes totally impossible deeds, led him to translate the art of building from the Temple of Solomon back to ancient Britain, where he founded a city around healing hot springs – the City of Bath.

11 Opposite page
The Origin of Building, or the Plagiarism of the Heathens Detected
John Wood the Elder
1738
Hand-written. Pen and ink on paper, bound
382 x 245 x 34mm

Bath Central Library, Bath & North East Somerset Council
B722, 50:1745, Fol. mss. SR

This is the second of two manuscript versions of Wood's *Origin of Building* and can be dated to c.1737, although it is highly likely that Wood began preparing the material for this work as early as 1730.

When published, *The Origin of Building* was divided into Four Books. However, the manuscript has a 5th unpublished Book in which Wood traces the Jewish origins of British architecture, looking especially at the primitive Christian churches in Britain.

The majority of the writing in the manuscript is in the hand of one, or possibly two clerks. The workings of the author's mind and the immediacy of his ideas are clearly seen in the slashing lines that cross out entire sentences and the hastily written amendments made by Wood himself.

The first manuscript version of Wood's *Origin of Building* is held at the Sir John Soane Museum, London. The collection also includes the copy of *The Origin of Building* owned by Sir William Chambers, which has annotations in Chambers' hand, and that believed to be Soane. CE Brownwell, *John Wood the Elder & John Wood the Younger*, unpublished PHD thesis, Columbia University, 1976. E Harris & N Savage, 'John Wood', *British Architectural Books and Writers 1556-1785*, Cambridge University Press, Cambridge, 1990, pp.480-489. T Mowl & B Earnshaw, *John Wood: Architect of Obsession*, Millstream Books, Bath, 1988.

Fig. 35
Noah's Ark, *The Antiquities of the Jews*, Flavius Josephus, 1733 edition

The Origin of Building

or the

Plagiarism of the Heathens

Detected

Being an Account in General of the Rise and Progress of Architecture from the Creation of the World to the Death of King Solomon and of its Advancement in Asia Egypt Greece Italy and Britain till it Arrive to its highest perfection

And containing in particular

An ample description not only of Noah's Ark the City and Tower of Babel Moses's Tabernacle and Solomon's Temple but of the Egyptian Edifices both publick and private the Citys of Nineveh Ecbatone and Babylon with the Palaces Temples Churches Monumental Pillars Obelisks and Pyramids erected in Asia and divers other Countrys

Extracted from History both Sacred and Profane

In which

The Cause of the Deluge, and Confusion of Languages, the Design and Nature of Urim and Thummim, and the manner in which the Jews were to be Instructed in the Law; are explained, the several parts of the Tabernacle and Temple are shewn to be an Emblematical Representation of the whole Jewish History; the Texts Relating to the piece of Arnon's Threshing floor, and the Length of Solomon's Brazen Pillars, are Reconciled. The Age of Terah at the Birth of Abraham is ascertained, and many of the seeming Contradictions in Holy Writ are cleared up so as to Render the Sacred and Profane Chronology certain and Reconcileable between the Reign of Nimrod at Babel and that of Alexander the Great; the Transfers of the Supreme Power and Collected Riches of the Earth from one Country to another, together with the Progress of Building, are Ranged in a proper Order of time; and from thence Sir Isaac Newton's System to amend the Chronology of Antient Kingdoms, appears to be Consistent with the Course of Great Events in all parts of the World; the Principles of Architecture, the proper Orders of Columns, the Forms and Proportions of Temples Basilicas, Churches and other Celebrated Edifices, as well Antient as Modern are likewise particularly explained; and demonstrated to have taken their Rise from the Works of the Jews, and not Grecians, as suggested by Pagan Writers and their Followers; And the Length of the Jewish Cubit as well as

66

In 1741 John Wood published his own treatise on architecture entitled *The Origin of Building, or the Plagiarism of the Heathens Detected.* As has been noted, the aim of this book was to prove that the origin of architecture could be found in the buildings erected by the Jews, and that all the temples and works of classical Greece and Rome were mere imitations of the edifices designed by God.

Noah's Ark was the first structure with dimensions defined by God, but it was not until Moses was directed to build the Tabernacle in the Wilderness that the essential architectural precepts of Strength, Convenience and Beauty were combined for the first time. The Tabernacle was a moveable structure of wooden pillars and curtains. In Wood's opinion, architecture was finally perfected when Solomon built the Temple in Jerusalem out of stone. From the Tabernacle and the Temple, Wood traces the development of architecture, illustrating how it was witnessed and copied by the Greeks, Romans and the Ancient Britons.

Other writers published on the biblical origins of building, but John Wood was the only one who was also an architect attempting to put his ideas into practice. Unfortunately, *The Origin of Building* was too idiosyncratically intellectual and weighed down with biblical facts to be of practical use to any architects other than Wood himself.

12 *The Complete Works*
Flavius Josephus
Book, printed by R Penny, London
This translation published 1733
350 x 235 x 75mm
Special Collections, Information Services, University of Bristol Library

Born in 37AD in Jerusalem, Flavius Josephus was a member of the priestly nobility and before his death in 101AD produced many works chronicling the history of the Jews. Only four of the works survive, including the *Antiquities of the Jews* in which the Temple of Solomon is described.

As they are our only source of knowledge on the history of the Jews in the first century, the works of Josephus have been translated many times. At one time the only book more widely read in Europe was the Bible.

Wood refers frequently to Josephus in his *Origin of Building* and it is most likely that Wood consulted either the 1733 or 1737 English translations.

12

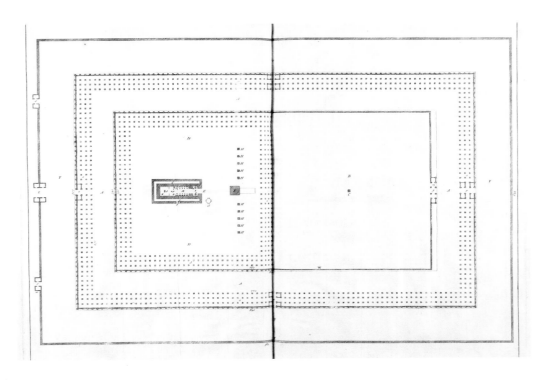

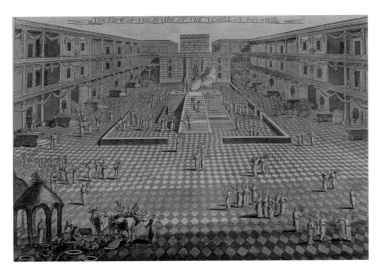

Fig. 36
Above: Plan of the Temple of Solomon, *The Origin of Building, or the Plagiarism of the Heathens Detected,* John Wood the Elder, 1741

Fig. 37
Left: the Interior of the Temple of Solomon, *The Complete Works,* Flavius Josephus, 1754 edition

The restoration of Solomon's Temple in Wales

In 1730 John Wood was commissioned to survey the ruinous shell of Llandaff Cathedral and after some debate was employed by the Bishop of Llandaff to rebuild the Cathedral in 1734. Wood believed that underneath the Gothic embellishments of the Middle Ages lay the remains of the most ancient church in Britain, and that its original dimensions were derived from Noah's Ark and Solomon's Temple. To prove this, Wood claimed that all the proportions of the original structure corresponded to the Doric order and drafted the plan of the original pre-medieval Llandaff in order to compare it to the plan of Solomon's Temple. It was this 'original' Cathedral that Wood restored.

Llandaff took almost 20 years to build and when finished produced the strange sight of a neo-classical church set within the ruins of a Gothic Cathedral.

Llandaff Cathedral underwent major alterations in the 19th century when most of Wood's work was demolished.

Fig. 38
Wood chose not to illustrate his work at Llandaff in any of his publications and any drawings that may have existed have since been lost. There are some small sketches in a notebook, compiled by William Cole that were copied from a letter between the Chapter Clerk of the Cathedral Thomas Davis and the antiquarian Browne Willis. By combining these drawings with accounts of the building before it was demolished, it is possible to reconstruct Wood's Llandaff Cathedral.

In 1931 such a reconstruction of Wood's 'Temple' at Llandaff Cathedral was undertaken, and the resultant drawings provide a good impression of what this temple, built inside a Gothic ruin, would have looked like.

Although written in 1743, the *Dissertation upon the Orders of Columns* was not published until 1750. It expands upon the ideas concerning the orders of architecture that Wood had set out to prove in *The Origin of Building*.

The book explains the origin and development of proportions relating to each of the orders, and includes illustrations of the various elements of each order. Compared to *The Origin of Building* this slim volume was a far more accessible, and therefore more practical work for the architect or builder.

See Cat. No. 11.

One of the most important elements of *The Origin of Building* was Wood's determination to prove that the three orders of architecture did not originate in classical antiquity, as Vitruvius decreed, but rather in the wooden pillars of the Tabernacle. They were then perfected in stone when Solomon built the Temple in Jerusalem. Thus Wood provides the Doric, the Ionic and the Corinthian with Jewish, as opposed to pagan origins.

The Israelites built cottages around the Tabernacle and the Temple, and to Wood, even these small structures could achieve the distinction of beauty through the application of the orders. He went on to build three such cottages himself, each one an essay in the orders of architecture.

13

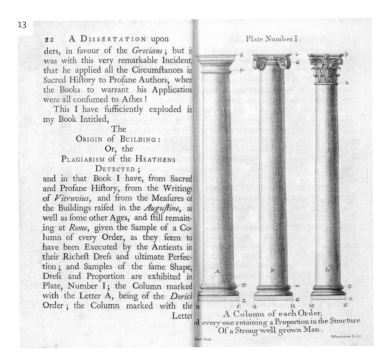

Fig. 39

The Strong – Lilliput Castle

Lilliput Castle was built on the slopes of Lansdown in 1738 for Jerry Peirce, a Bath surgeon fond of parties who was in search of a small townhouse suitable for a bachelor.

Of the three Villas, Lilliput (actually built second) is most similar to the designs for the Tabernacle Cottages that Wood illustrated in *The Origin of Building*.

The Doric is not obviously apparent in the design of Lilliput. However, Wood claimed that the fact the house was not completely destroyed during a fire (which occurred shortly after it was built) proved Lilliput's Doric strength.

Fig. 40

The Mean – Belcomb Brook Villa

Belcomb Brook Villa was built just outside Bath – near Bradford-on-Avon – in 1734 for Mr & Mrs Francis Yerbury.

Built as an extension to an existing building, Belcomb was originally conceived not as a family home, but as a retreat for a newly married couple.

In the garden front at Belcomb, Wood created a clearly defined essay in the Ionic order, with pilasters and pedimented windows providing the Villa with an elegant yet understated grandeur.

Fig. 41

The Delicate – Titan Barrow Loggia

The last of Wood's Villas, Titan Barrow, was built in 1748 at Bathford for Southwell Piggott.

As with the previous Villas, Titan Barrow was based on the cube and triangular pediment of the Tabernacle cottages, only this time Wood extended the cube by adding a further bay to each side.

Although largely altered since it was built, the garden front of Titan Barrow survives almost as Wood designed it. With three-quarter columns and correct decorative details, at Titan Barrow Wood successfully illustrated the 'delicate' nature of the Corinthian order.

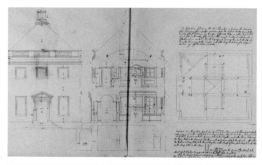

Fig. 39

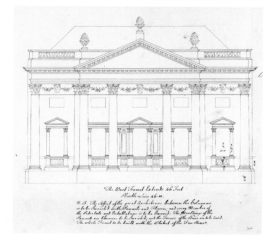

Fig. 40

Fig. 41

The reality and eminence of King Bladud

By the time *The Origin of Building* had been published Wood's thoughts had begun to move away from the Jews. He started working on a new project, one that would be his most famous publication. It is a personal manifesto in which we are given a clear insight into his ideas, through his own words.

In *An Essay Towards a Description of Bath,* Wood traced how the Druids, influenced by the Jewish models, developed architecture in Britain. To do this he elaborated the legend of Bladud, claiming that he was present at the building of the second temple in Jerusalem, was also the Hyperborean priest who taught Pythagoras, was responsible for bringing the ideas of architecture to the Druids and finally founded the city of Bath.

14

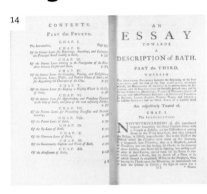

14 *An Essay Towards a Description of Bath,* Vol. I
John Wood the Elder
1749, 2nd edition
200 x 130 x 20mm
Bath Preservation Trust
41G

15 *An Essay Towards a Description of Bath,* Vol. II
John Wood the Elder
Published 1749, 2nd edition
200 x 130 x 20mm
Bath Preservation Trust
41G

The first volume of Wood's *An Essay Towards a Description of Bath* was published in 1742, with the second volume quickly following in 1743. There is also a third volume, published in 1743, of which only one rare copy survives in Bath Central Library.

It is obvious that as Wood was completing *The Origin of Building* he had already begun to form the work that would become the *Essay.* Even when it was first published Wood must have felt there was more to add, so in 1749 he published the amended second edition, in which an engraving of the stately figure of Bladud is included.

See Cat. No. 11. W Ison, *The Georgian Buildings of Bath 1700–1830,* 1948, (second edition 1980). RS Neale, *Bath, A Social History,* Routledge & Kegan Paul, 1981.

15

4. John Wood's vision for Bath

'I began to turn my thoughts towards the Improvement of the City by Building'

John Wood, *An Essay Towards a Description of Bath*

74

John Wood tells us that at the age of 21 he had his vision for Bath. He returned to his home city in 1727, to what he believed was once the most important settlement in ancient Britain, but which had subsequently become a small medieval collection of buildings and baths surrounding the Abbey and encased by walls.

Wood wanted to take this ruin, the remnants of a glorious ancient age, and rebuild it, restoring the city to its former magnificence, thereby creating a New Jerusalem in England, a 'Troy Novant'. To do this he envisaged a series of three monumental building projects: an Imperial Gymnasium, a Royal Forum and a Grand Circus.

Despite being continually obstructed by the Bath City Corporation, landowners and moneymen, Wood set about building this ideal city with the fervour of a man determined to achieve both his architectural ambitions and his entrepreneurial aspirations.

Continually educating himself in order to refine his architectural beliefs, Wood soon combined his long established passion for Palladianism with two further obsessions: a growing interest in Ancient British history, and the constant yet mysterious presence of Freemasonry.

In the space of 26 years, and fuelled by these three obsessions, John Wood attempted to create a new Bath in order to realise his vision.

16 *The Four Bath Worthies*
Anonymous
c.1735
Oil on canvas
1125 x 1375mm
Bath Preservation Trust
355P

The title of this painting, which was found in pencil on the rear of the canvas, refers to the importance and prominence of the Bath men it is believed to depict.

On the right stands John Wood in surveyor's clothes with an architectural drawing or deed tucked under his arm, and next to him sits Robert Gay, who inherited the manor of Walcot in 1699, making him one of Bath's major landowners. To the left of Gay, also seated, is Ralph Allen, the owner of the Combe Down stone quarries and Wood's patron-client. The fourth figure is Richard Jones, the Clerk of Works who eventually replaced Wood as the builder-surveyor of Allen's mansion house, Prior Park.

76

When John Wood returned to Bath in the spring of 1727 he began working on projects for two very significant clients: James Brydges the Duke of Chandos (1674-1744) and Ralph Allen (1693-1764).

Chandos owned a considerable amount of land in Bath and was keen to develop the area around the old almshouses of St John's Hospital. Wood named this project in his *Essay* as 'Chandos Court', a collection of six houses around a central courtyard garden. Although the Court was not completed as Wood had envisaged it, he re-built the main structure of St John's Hospital, and four buildings to serve as lodgings houses for fashionable visitors to Bath.

In spite of the experience he gained in London and Yorkshire, Wood was still lacking in expert practical knowledge, draughting skills and the ability to direct his workforce. St John's was riddled with problems: from disgruntled workers claiming they could not understand the architect's drawings, to an irritated Duke when Wood's designs for the plumbing proved disastrous. The project taught the young Wood vital lessons, and from that point onwards, although designed by him, the practical construction of Wood's buildings in Bath would be either subleased to other builders or controlled by a clerk of works.

Ralph Allen was one of Bath's most famous residents. He had amassed great wealth through his reorganisation of the postal system, and he used that wealth to buy up the Bath freestone quarries that lined the southern hills of the city. In 1727 he commissioned an extension to his existing townhouse in Lilliput Alley. Although there is no firm proof that Wood was responsible for the design of the addition, he lays claim to it subtly in the *Essay*. Wood was also the only architect in Bath at the time that could design something so wholly Palladian in concept.

Wood's first Palladian designs for Bath

Fig. 42
Above: entrance to St John's Hospital, Bath

Fig. 43
Below: façade of Ralph Allen's Town House

17 *East View of Ralph Allen's Town House*
Henry Venn Lansdown
1855
Pen and sepia wash
244 x 350mm
Victoria Art Gallery, Bath &
North East Somerset Council
BATVG PD:1926.28

17

This view of Ralph Allen's Town House clearly shows the façade attributed to Wood. It was built in 1727 as part of an extension to the existing building. The condensed façade echoes the ostentation of the Baroque and pre-empts the Palladian mansion that Wood would design for Allen on the southern slopes of Bath.

For the Town House see M Forsyth, *Bath*, Pevsner Architectural Guides, Yale University Press, 2004. W Ison, *The Georgian Buildings of Bath 1700-1830*, 1948, (second edition 1980).

18 *Chandos House, Bath*
Henry Venn Lansdown
c.1855
Pen and sepia wash
249 x 330mm
Victoria Art Gallery, Bath &
North East Somerset Council
BATVG PD:1926.103

Not illustrated

Chandos House was built between 1729-30 as part of Wood's Chandos Court development. It clearly illustrates the simple boldness of Wood's early Palladian designs.

Henry Venn Lansdown is perhaps most famous for his posthumous publication *Recollections of the late William Beckford, 1893*. In the mid-19th century Lansdown produced a series of pencil and wash drawings of buildings in Bath. These views are important as they often depict buildings that have either been destroyed or vastly altered.

19 *Ralph Allen's Town House*
Ros Hudson
1978
Architectural model in birch plywood, jelutong and obeche
600 x 270 x 270mm
Crisp Cowley Chartered Surveyors, Bath

See Cat. No. 17

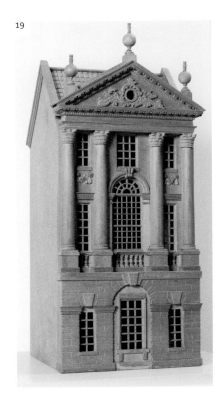

19

78 Built between 1728-36, Queen Square was the first major project successfully completed by John Wood in Bath. At Queen Square Wood created not just a building, but an entire space within the city.

Influenced by what he had seen being projected for the great squares in London and by Colen Campbell's designs for Wanstead House, Wood embarked on building his own Palladian palace: a row of terraced townhouses united by a single façade.

Of the four ranges that make up Queen Square, Wood's greatest triumph is the elegant north side, defined by the central portico, which is supported by Giant columns of the Corinthian order.

Queen Square

Fig. 44
Queen Square, Bath

20 *Original balustrade and die from Queen Square*
Maker unknown
c.1732
Oolitic limestone, Combe Down Quarry, Bath
Dimensions:
Die 560 x 450 x 250mm
Die 560 x 450 x 255mm
Balustrade 900 x 1385 x 275mm
Building of Bath Museum
E.0071
(1993:67/1993:68/2004:001)

When first built the central space of Queen Square was enclosed, not by the iron railings that can be seen today, but by an elegant stone balustrade. Made up of rectangular die and balusters, the balustrading was removed to a local garden in 1775. These fragments were rescued and given to the Bath Preservation Trust in 1972.

The two rectangular 'die' are very significant items. Both have carved into them Wood's original plan for Queen Square; one has since been used as a sundial, while the other records masons marks and the exact date when the balustrading was removed: 8 August 1775.

21 *Queen Square*
Michael Bishop
1993
Architectural model made
of plywood and card
980 x 730 x 150mm
Building of Bath Museum
E.0093/1993:28

This model clearly shows the
concessions Wood had to make
to his original design of Queen
Square. Sir John Buckworth's
elaborate villa set back from the
west side interrupted Wood's
plan for four uniform sides to the
Square. In 1830, John Pinch the
Younger filled the gap between
the two end houses in the Greek
Revival style.

The south side of Queen Square
was badly damaged during the
bombing raids of the Second
World War, and has been
extensively repaired. It is now
the Francis in the Park Hotel.
It was on this side that John
Wood lived, providing him with
the perfect view across the
square to his great palace front.

Having learnt from the mistakes of Chandos Court, Wood initiated a form of construction that would not only make him a wealthy man, but also come to shape the entire city. Speculative building meant that while Wood leased the land from Robert Gay for £137 per annum, each individual house or plot was then subleased to other individual builders or masons. They would be responsible for the form of the house built behind the façade, as long as the exterior elevation conformed to Wood's design. Ultimately this meant less work and expense for Wood and, by claiming £305 per annum in rents, a tidy profit of £168 per year.

In the Queen Square garden Wood intended the path between nature and building to be a natural progression of the gaze. The space was quartered and divided by gravel and turf paths. At the centre of the garden he placed a basin of water from which rose the Obelisk erected in 1738 by Richard 'Beau' Nash (1674-1762) and originally 70ft high. Wood planned low espaliers of limes and elms. Unlike the present trees in the Square, they would not have towered so high as to diminish the visual effect of the surrounding buildings.

21

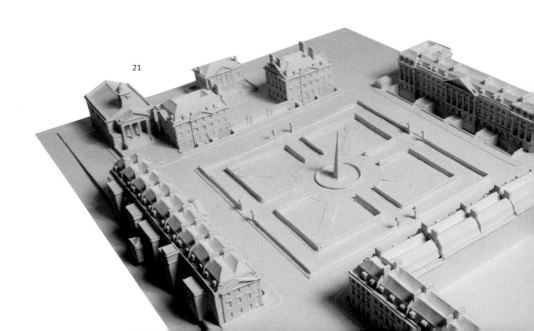

22

22 *Entrance to St Mary's Chapel, Queen Square*
Henry Venn Lansdown
c.1855
Pen and sepia wash
246 x 310mm
Victoria Art Gallery, Bath &
North East Somerset Council
BATVG PD:1926.32

This view clearly shows that the turret seen in Wood's designs for St Mary's did not exist in the mid-19th century. This has led to speculations over whether the bell turret was actually built. However, the Thomas Robins sketch made before 1775, clearly shows the Chapel complete with turret [see page 83].

For another rare view of St Mary's in which the bell turret can be made out see J Lees-Milne & D Ford, *Images of Bath*, St Helena Press, 1982, Cat. 771.

Fig. 45
Plan of Queen Square, John
Wood the Elder, *An Essay Towards
a Description of Bath*

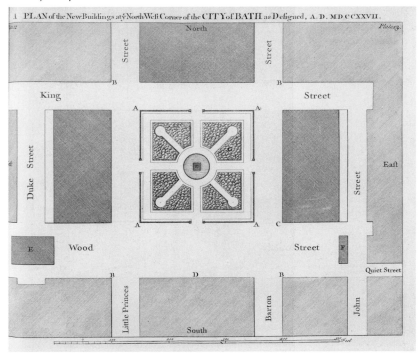

23 *Queen Square Chapel*
John Wood the Elder
1732
Pencil and ink wash
291 x 455mm
Victoria Art Gallery, Bath &
North East Somerset Council
BATVG PD:1918.1092

Originally situated on the west
side of Queen Square, St Mary's
was the first proprietary chapel to
be built in Bath. Wood proposed
erecting a chapel for the use of
residents of Queen Square and
the surrounds in 1732. Eleven
subscribers, including Wood
himself, contributed £60
towards the chapel, which
opened for service in 1734.

The entrance front is defined by
an imposing Doric portico, while
the interior of St Mary's was even
more impressive, with 12 Ionic
columns approximately 17ft
high. St Mary's was demolished
c.1875 when Chapel Row was
widened to provide better access
to Green Park Station.

For many years five fragments of
the internal columns lay near the
Chapel site; they were rescued in
1995 and can be today seen in
the courtyard of the Building of
Bath Museum.

John Wood, *An Essay Towards A Description of
Bath*, 2nd edition, 1749, Vol. II, pp.312-315.
W Ison, *The Georgian Buildings of Bath 1700-
1830*, 1948, (Second edition 1980). T Mowl &
B Earnshaw, *John Wood: Architect of Obsession*,
Millstream Books, Bath, 1988, pp.72-77.

24 *Queen Square, Bath*
Anonymous
Before 1830
Pencil on paper
173 x 273mm
Victoria Art Gallery, Bath &
North East Somerset Council
BATVGPD:1991.61

Not illustrated

This view of Queen Square can be
dated to between the removal of
the stone balustrading in 1775
and the filling in of the central
gap between the end houses on
the west side by John Pinch the
Younger in 1830.

23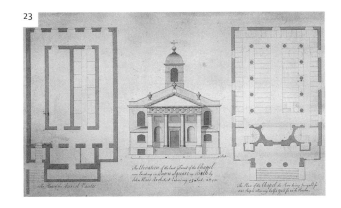

'For the Intention of a Square
in a City is for People to
assemble together'

John Wood, *An Essay Towards a Description of Bath*

25

25 *Queen Square, Bath*
Thomas Malton the Younger
1784
Aquatint
328 x 476mm
Victoria Art Gallery, Bath &
North East Somerset Council
BATVG PD:1926.232

Original watercolour illustrated

Thomas Malton the Younger
(1748-1804) was the son of an
architectural draughtsman and
perspective lecturer. He became
famous for his topographical
views of London. From 1783
Malton was a drawing master at
the Royal Academy and between
1789-90 his most eminent pupil
was the young JMW Turner.

Malton visited Bath in 1777 and
produced a series of watercolours
depicting the great buildings and
views of the city. These views
were reproduced extensively as
aquatints. The original
watercolours are held at the
Victoria Art Gallery, Bath.

J Lees-Milne & D Ford, *Images of Bath*,
St Helena Press, 1982, Cat. 501.

Opposite page
Fig. 46
Top: *Elevation of the North side
of Queen Square, Bath.* John Wood
the Elder

Fig. 47
Middle, left: *Elevation of the
South side of Queen Square, Bath.*
John Wood the Elder

Fig. 48
Middle, right: *The West & South
sides of Queen Square, Bath.*
Thomas Robins, c.1757-9

Fig. 49
Below, right: *The West & North
sides of Queen Square, Bath.*
Thomas Robins, c.1757-9

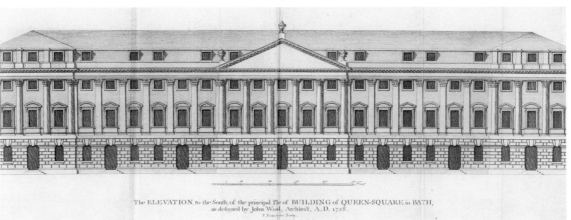

The ELEVATION, to the South, of the principal Pile of BUILDING of QUEEN-SQUARE in BATH,
as designed by John Wood, Architect, A.D. 1728.
P. Fourdrinier Sculp.

Prior Park

In his designs for Ralph Allen's house at Prior Park, Wood once again turned to Colen Campbell's Wanstead House for inspiration. Sited upon a terrace in the hillside, Prior Park is a stage-set designed to display the qualities and beauty of Bath stone. The theatrical nature of the house also created a seat from which Allen could look out across the valley and see the glory of Bath grow as Wood re-built the city in stone mined from Allen's quarries.

The plan of Prior Park published by Wood in the 1749 edition of the *Essay* clearly shows what he originally intended. The house was to be flanked by two identical wings, linked by an arcade punctuated with square pavilions. This vision for the site was never achieved. Following disagreements with Allen over alterations to his designs, Wood left Prior Park with only the basement storey completed, leaving Allen's Clerk of Works, Richard Jones, to finish the house.

Jones' alterations and wings never achieved the elegance of Wood's design, and later 19th century additions and alterations destroyed the symmetry Wood had intended.

In spite of this, Wood's overall vision for Prior Park was still fulfilled because of the position of the house itself within the landscape. Wood intended Prior Park to make up three sides of a theoretical giant dodecagon, a twelve-sided geometrical figure. It is another example of Wood creating a space through the combination of individual structures, nature and geometry.

Fig. 50
Left: Prior Park, Bath

Fig. 51
Above: Prior Park, Bath

Fig. 52
Right: Elevation of the north front, Prior Park, John Wood the Elder

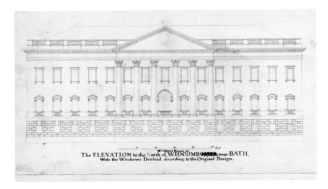

The ELEVATION to the North of WIDCOMB near BATH,
With the Windows Dressed according to the Original Design.

86   In the 18th century architectural drawings rarely
      survived the building process. As a result, the
      majority of drawings that exist by John Wood
      depict unrealised projects and unexecuted
      buildings. However, by using what does survive it
      is possible to trace the progress from initial ideas
      to working drawings, and from finished drawings
      to the engraved plates published in Wood's books.

The drawings of John Wood

26

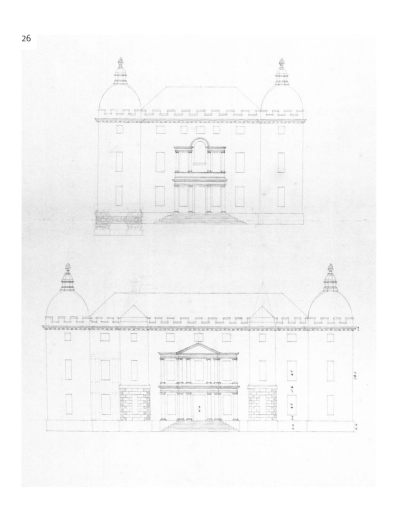

26 *Bound book of 84 original
    architectural drawings*
    **John Wood the Elder and
    John Wood the Younger**
    1737-1749
    Pen and ink on paper
    360 x 305 x 45mm
    Bath Central Library, Bath &
    North East Somerset Council
    B728, 23039, SR 4

The drawings in this volume
span a period in the 1740s when
Wood's working relationship
with his son was extremely
constructive. Included in the
volume are the contract drawings
for Titan Barrow Loggia, the
preparatory drawings for
engravings of Prior Park, as well
as designs for Buckland House,
Berkshire, built by Wood the
Younger. The book also contains
designs for unknown and
unexecuted projects and includes
several drawings for bridges, villas,
churches and chimneypieces.

The pages illustrated are part
of a set of drawings that depict
several variations of plans and
elevations for a part-castellated
building, worked on by both
Wood and his son.

T Mowl & B Earnshaw, *John Wood: Architect
of Obsession*, Millstream Books, Bath, 1988,
Chapter 11.

27 *Letter*
From John Wood to William Brydges
Dated 27 April 1734
Pen and ink on paper
230 x 370mm
Bath Central Library, Bath &
North East Somerset Council
AL 1265

In 1734 Wood was working at
Tyberton Court in Herefordshire
for William Brydges, second
cousin of James Brygdes, Duke
of Chandos. This letter, written
by Wood from Bath, describes
for Brydges the recent visit to
the city by the Prince of Orange.

It records a true sample of Wood's
strong and bold handwriting, as
well as his distinctive signature.

28 *Design for a merchant's house,
Bath (elevation)*
John Wood the Elder
c.1745
Pen and ink wash on paper
230 x 350mm
RIBA Library Drawings Collection
SC 110/12 (9)

27

water so if you have not ordered him to be paid I will take care him. I have forgot what his demand is but what I paid is as

Augt. 29th 1732 Carridge of 6 dozen of Water to Bath .... 0 : 6 : 0
                 3 Hampers .... 0 : 3 : 0
                 Packing .... 0 : 1 : 0
Septr. 4   Carridge to Bristol .... 0 : 3 : 6
                                                  £ 0 : 13 : 6

I am Sr.

Yr. most obedt. & most hum: Servt.

Jo: Wood

28

29 *Design for a merchant's house, Bath (plan)*
John Wood the Elder
c.1745
Pen and ink wash on paper
230 x 350mm
RIBA Library Drawings Collection
SC110/12 (7)

These are the only two drawings by Wood held at the RIBA Library Drawings Collection and for many years they remained unattributed to the architect. They are designs for a house in Abbey Street, on the land belonging to the Duke of Kingston, south-east of Bath Abbey.

Abbey Street was planned in the 1740s to link Abbey Churchyard to Abbey Green. This house is believed to have been built in 1760, possibly under the direction of John Wood the Younger. Research has produced credible evidence to prove that this is the house in which the artist Thomas Gainsborough (1727-1788) lived and worked between 1760 and 1766, before he moved to his more famous address in the Circus.

J Ayres, *Building the Georgian City, Bath Spa*, Bath Preservation Trust, 1991. J Harris, *The Palladians*, RIBA Drawings Collection/Trefoil Books, London, 1981, pp.102. S Slomon, Gainsborough and the Lodging House Way, *Gainsborough's House Society Annual Report* 1991/2, pp.22-44 and *Gainsborough in Bath*, Yale University Press, New Haven & London, 2002, pp.52-3.

29

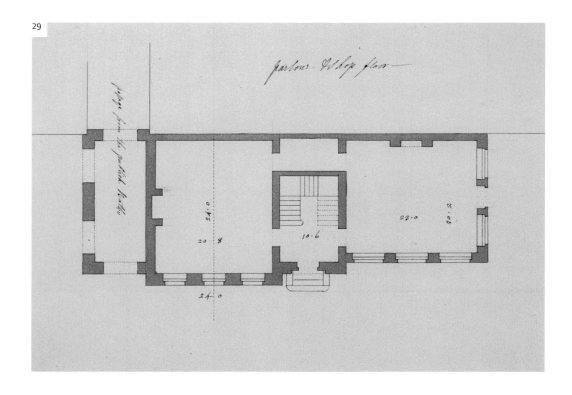

30 *Elevation of the Bristol Exchange*
Pierre Fourdrinier after
John Wood
1744-5
Copperplate engraving
223 x 275mm
Building of Bath Museum
E 0561

31 *Elevation of the Bristol Exchange*
as it fronts North to the Peristyle
Pierre Fourdrinier after
John Wood
1744-5
Copperplate engraving
200 x 258mm
Building of Bath Museum
E 0562

32 *Elevation of the Bristol Exchange*
as it fronts South to the Peristyle
Pierre Fourdrinier after
John Wood
1744-5
Copperplate engraving
197 x 245mm
Building of Bath Museum
E 0563

These engravings appear to be proofs for three of the engraved plates in John Wood's *A Description of the Exchange of Bristol*. Several amendments can be seen in Wood's hand, after which these plates were most probably returned to the engraver. Wood used Pierre Fourdrinier as the engraver in all his publications. Based in London, Fourdrinier was one of the most accomplished copperplate engravers of his day, and was responsible for plates in many publications by the country's leading architects.

These engravings were recently discovered in the archives of the late Walter Ison held at the Building of Bath Museum.

A collection of drawings, letters and notes by Wood and his son regarding Bristol Exchange can be found in the archives of the Royal Academy Library. John Wood, *A Description of the Exchange of Bristol*, 1745 (see Cat. No. 33). W Ison, *The Georgian Buildings of Bristol*, Faber & Faber Ltd, 1952; reprinted 1978.

30

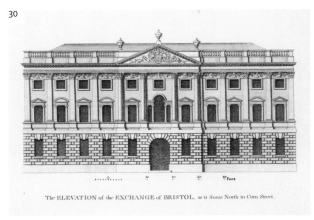

The ELEVATION of the EXCHANGE of BRISTOL, as it fronts North to Corn Street.

31

The ELEVATION of the EXCHANGE of BRISTOL, as it fronts North to the PERISTYLE of that Structure.
Together with
The SECTION of the Building on each side the PERISTYLE.

32

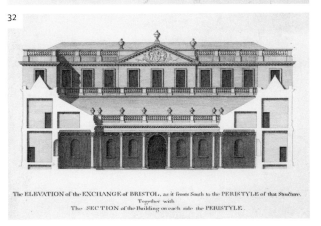

The ELEVATION of the EXCHANGE of BRISTOL, as it fronts South to the PERISTYLE of that Structure,
Together with
The SECTION of the Building on each side the PERISTYLE.

90   33

A
DESCRIPTION
OF THE
EXCHANGE
OF
BRISTOL:
Wherein the Ceremony of
LAYING the FIRST STONE of that
STRUCTURE;
Together with That of
OPENING the BUILDING
FOR
PUBLICK USE,
Is particularly Recited.

By JOHN WOOD, Architect.

BATH:
Printed in the Year MDCCXLV.

And Sold by J. LEAKE; C. HITCH, in Pater-noster-Row,
London; and B. HICKEY, in Bristol.

33 *A Description of the Exchange
of Bristol*
John Wood
Published 1745
Printed book
Printed in Bath
246 x 132 x 15mm
Bath Central Library, Bath &
North East Somerset Council
B725.25 WOO, 23151, LS 8vo

Published two years after the
completion of the building,
this slim volume records in
detail the disagreements
Wood encountered during
the construction of the Bristol
Exchange.

What the book does not outline
are the events leading up to the
acceptance of Wood's designs.
The architect, William Halfpenny,
had been working on designs for
the Exchange for some time, but
as the building was to represent
the power and strength of the
city, they were not considered
to be elegant enough by the
Corporation. Wood's designs
were presented only one week
after he was invited to submit
them. This suggests that he had
been working on ideas for the
Exchange for some time,
probably following discussions
with Ralph Allen who provided
all the stone for the building.

A Foyle, *Bristol*, Pevsner Architectural Guides,
Yale University Press, New Haven & London,
2004. E Harris & N Savage, 'John Wood',
*British Architectural Books and Writers 1556-
1785*, Cambridge University Press, Cambridge,
1990, pp.480-489. T Mowl & B Earnshaw,
John Wood: Architect of Obsession, Millstream
Books, Bath, 1988, Chapter 10.

John Wood the Masterplanner
Imperial Gymnasium

John Wood's masterplan for Bath was made up of three components or structures through which the glory of Ancient Bath would be reclaimed by the modern city. These were an Imperial Gymnasium, a Royal Forum and a Grand Circus.

Individually each structure had a definite function, but collectively they would re-shape the physical appearance of the city and provide Bath with a procession of monumental spaces, the size and impact of which would determine the form of the city for the future.

When John Wood returned to Bath in 1727 he began working on the structures that would collectively form his Imperial Gymnasium.

Central to the project was the construction of a new General Hospital. Wood proposed two designs for the building, one quadrangular, one circular. Years of negotiations regarding land subscriptions and design ensued. Finally, in 1738, the site was approved and final designs were agreed upon. The idea for a circular hospital had been abandoned, instead Wood constructed a lacklustre rectangular block that was completed and opened in 1741.

Whilst working on his ideas for the hospital Wood surveyed the existing city baths. Finding them in a 'wretched and dangerous condition' he proposed to enlarge and renovate the King's and Queen's baths, making them more accessible to the public and joining them to the new hospital.

By physically linking these structures Wood was trying to establish his Imperial Gymnasium, but what form or shape that structure would have taken is unknown. The only element he ever constructed was the General Hospital, now the Bath Mineral Water Hospital.

Fig. 53
The Mineral Water Hospital

John Wood's most elaborate and monumental design was also his greatest failure. The Royal Forum, had it been built, would have completely altered the direction in which the city was to expand, and its presence in Bath would have overshadowed even the Circus and Crescent. It was Wood at his most visionary.

The rare third edition of Wood's *An Essay Towards a Description of Bath* has the only visual evidence of what he envisaged for the Royal Forum. A massive rectangular space measuring 1,040ft long by 624ft wide, the Forum would have been bisected by the canalised Avon, at the centre of which Wood planned a huge octagonal basin of water. Around the sides of the Forum would have been 50ft wide terraces, and behind them, rows of buildings all looking down onto the vast open space.

Only a small corner of Wood's Royal Forum was ever completed. North Parade, South Parade, Duke Street and Pierrepont Street exist as a mere 'wing' of this space, originally designed to equal the magnificence of the ancients. This is a very small remnant of what would have been John Wood's greatest achievement had it ever been realised.

The Royal Forum

34 *Deed*
Signed by John Wood, Gentleman of Queen Square and Francis Fauquier, Gentleman of Queen Square
Signed 30 October 1739
Manuscript
675 x 660mm
Building of Bath Museum
E 0564
Not illustrated

This deed relates to the plot on Wood's Grand Parade (or North Parade) stretching 73ft east from Duke Street towards the Avon. Attached can be seen Wood's drawing for the ground floor plan of the property to be leased and built by Fauquier.

It is interesting to note that Fauquier, like Wood, is recorded as living in Queen Square. Several of the leaseholders from Queen Square also took on properties in the Parades. Ralph Allen himself, having missed the opportunity to lease the grandest house on Queen Square, lost no time in obtaining from Wood the best position on Grand Parade.

35 *The South Parade of Bath*
Thomas Malton the Younger
c.1784
Aquatint
327 x 475mm
Victoria Art Gallery, Bath &
North East Somerset Council
BATVG PD:1926.233

Original watercolour illustrated

South Parade made up the north corner of the Royal Forum. It is this façade that would have looked down over the open space of the Forum. Wood proposed to build an Assembly Room at terrace level on South Parade with a theatre in the basement.

J Lees-Milne & D Ford, *Images of Bath*, St Helena Press, 1982, Cat. 612.

36 *The North Parade at Bath*
James Gandon after Thomas Malton the Younger
1779
Aquatint
319 x 472mm
Victoria Art Gallery, Bath & North East Somerset Council
BATVG PD:2000.83

Original watercolour illustrated

North Parade, or Grand Parade as Wood referred to it, comprises three blocks of buildings separated by Duke Street and Pierrepont Street. Wood intended this edifice to have a similar magnificence as the north side of Queen Square, and designed it to be rich in ornamentation. As always, his design was altered by the demands of the leaseholders, mainly Ralph Allen, and the enrichments were filtered out.

Wood intended the terrace walk of Grand Parade to become a place of promenading, overlooking the garden he had designed for St James's Triangle (later built as Parade Gardens).

J Lees-Milne & D Ford, *Images of Bath*, St Helena Press, 1982, Cat. 604.

35

36

'It shall represent the Forum or Places amoung the Ancients, where Kings were wont to Convene the People'

John Wood, *An Essay Towards a Description of Bath*

37

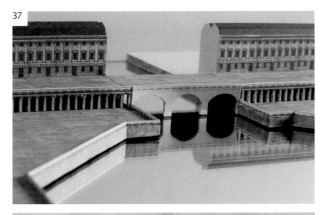

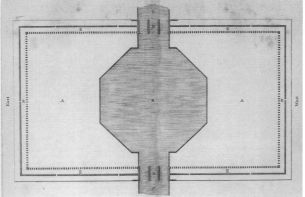

37 *Royal Forum*
Theo Dales
2004
Architectural model, MDF,
paper, mirror
730 x 570 x 70mm
Building of Bath Museum
E.0565

The only sources that exist for
the design of Wood's Royal
Forum are a ground plan and a
brief description, both of which
can be found in the rare third
volume of *An Essay Towards a
Description of Bath*.

This model, proposing what
the Forum would have looked
like had it been built, was
constructed using these sources
alongside knowledge of Wood's
other designs, both built and
unexecuted. In Wood's *Book of
Drawings* [Cat. No. 26] there are
several designs for bridges that
are believed to be for the Royal
Forum. These designs were also
used in the construction of this
model.

Fig. 54
Above: Plan of the Royal Forum,
John Wood the Elder, *An Essay
Towards a Description of Bath*,
Vol III, 1743

Fig. 55
Below: Plan of Bath Showing
the New Square on the Ham,
John Wood the Elder, 1740

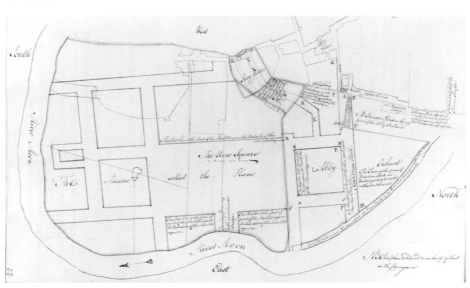

The Grand Circus

38

John Wood's Grand Circus is one of Bath's most famous landmarks. It is also the most widely discussed and debated.

Wood always wanted to construct a circular building in Bath, and in 1754 a terrace was sliced into Lansdown Hill and construction began on the Circus. Three months after the foundation stone was laid John Wood died leaving his son to complete his work.

There are many ways to interpret the Circus and many things that can be read in its façade. Often mistakenly believed to be based on the Colosseum in Rome, the Circus is actually the creation of all John Wood's obsessions. The influence of the ancient stone circles of the Druids, the subtle presence of Freemasonic symbolism and the sheer force of over 600 columns, all fuse together and bombard the visitor with a mass of visual stimulants.

However, the iconography of the building should never be disengaged from the overall effect and strength of Wood's design. Imagine the Circus as Wood intended it to be, without the trees in the centre, just a paved open space. Unlike Queen Square or the Royal Forum, the Circus was envisaged as a structure where the only element of nature to be found was the sky above. It was a dramatic and theatrical space where the architecture took centre stage.

What is perhaps more important than attempting to find answers or prove the truth behind this building, is to consider the many questions that its design creates. It is the veil of mystery and the assortment of possibilities behind Wood's design which creates the unmistakable atmosphere of awe and wonder that makes the Circus so imposing, intriguing and unique.

38 *The King's Circus at Bath*
Thomas Malton the Younger
1784
Aquatint
328 x 478mm
Victoria Art Gallery, Bath & North East Somerset Council
BATVG PD:1926.231

Original watercolour illustrated

J Lees-Milne & D Ford, *Images of Bath*, St Helena Press, 1982, Cat.. 515.

Fig. 56
Comparative section of
the Colosseum, Rome and
elevation of the Circus, Bath.
George Bailey, 1814

98

According to John Wood there had always been a temple to the sun and one to the moon on Lansdown. Wood wanted to restore these lost temples and use their magnificence to proclaim the glory of the modern city. To do this he designed two buildings, one in the form of the sun, the other a crescent moon.

What started as an interest in tracing the origin of architecture in Britain, developed into an obsession. John Wood saw in the stone circles of Stonehenge and Stanton Drew the architecture derived from Moses' Tabernacle and Solomon's Temple, transferred to Britain by the legendary King Bladud.

Through extensive surveys of these stone monuments, Wood calculated measurements that connected them to the dimensions of the sacred biblical structures. Most significantly, through manipulating his measurements of both Stonehenge and Stanton Drew, Wood found circles of standing stones with diameters of 316ft, which, by including surrounding ditches, could be calculated to 318ft. The diameter of the Circus in Bath is exactly 318ft.

Obsession: Ancient British history

39 *The Most Notable Antiquity of Great Britain, Vulgarly called Stone-Heng Restor'd*
Inigo Jones
1655
Book, printed by James Flesher, England
290 x 185mm
Special Collections, Information Services, University of Bristol Library

In 1620 Inigo Jones was instructed by James I to produce a report on Stonehenge. Following his initial report back to the Monarch, Jones appears to have continued investigating the stones out of his own interest and collected the raw materials for this book.

Stone-Heng Restor'd was published posthumously in 1655 by Jones' pupil, John Webb. Webb clearly stated that the book was in a 'rude' and 'indigested' form, apparently having been taken from the original manuscript that remained practically unaltered.

Jones ascribes the stones to the work of the Romans, not the Druids or Ancient British, for the reason that 'academies of design were unknown to them'.

E Harris & N Savage, 'Inigo Jones', *British Architectural Books and Writers 1556-1785*, Cambridge University Press, Cambridge, 1990, pp.247-252.

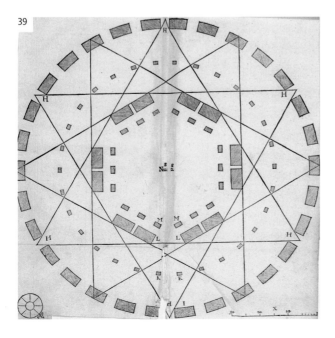

39

40 *Itinerarium Curiosum,* Vol. II
William Stukeley
1776
Book, printed by Baker & Leigh,
London
360 x 230 x 50mm
Special Collections, Information
Services, University of Bristol
Library
Gift of Joan Eyles

First published in 1724 William
Stukeley's *Itinerarium Curiosum*
(Itinerary of Curiosities) was
compiled during, and as a result
of, his travels around Britain.

Whilst he was undergoing his
medical training at Cambridge,
Stukeley (1687-1765) became
interested in topographical and
historical work, as well as ancient
relics. In 1730 Stukeley was
ordained, and the combination
of a career in the Church with
an interest for antiquities
encouraged him to publish
works often regarded as poetic
religious fantasies. He related
Druidism to the Church of
England and even gave himself
the title of Arch Druid.

When John Wood published
his own book on Stonehenge
Stukeley attacked it violently,
claiming it contained 'fabulous
whimseys of a crack'd
imagination'. To Stukeley,
Britain's greatest antiquarian,
it was 'an indigested farrago'
written by a 'quack in antiquity'!

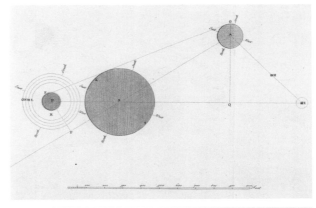

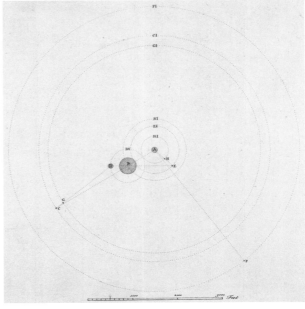

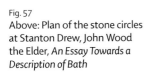

Fig. 57
Above: Plan of the stone circles
at Stanton Drew, John Wood
the Elder, *An Essay Towards a
Description of Bath*

Fig. 58
Below: General plan of Stanton
Drew. John Wood the Elder,
*An Essay Towards a Description
of Bath*

100

41

41 *Stonehenge*
**Phase III (early Bronze Age),
c.BC1500**
Alexander Siburn
1988
Fibreglass model
50 x 640 x 640mm
Wiltshire Heritage Museum

This model is one of a series of
six displayed at the Wiltshire
Heritage Museum, Devizes,
illustrating the stages in
development and construction
of Stonehenge.

The basic geometry of
Stonehenge cannot be denied as
having obvious influence on the
building of Wood's Circus. At
Stonehenge Wood recognised
the important forms of the full
outer circle of stones, and the
inner crescent shape (actually a
horseshoe). These were
significant forms in a temple
where the centre point is revered
as the precise location for solar
and lunar observation.

42 *Choir Gaure*
John Wood the Elder
1747
Book, printed in Oxford
220 x 132 x 15mm
Bath Central Library, Bath &
North East Somerset Council
LS.W936.2 WOO 8vo

In 1740 John Wood was
commissioned by his old London
patron, the Earl of Oxford, to
produce a report on Stonehenge.
In the Michaelmas of that year,
Wood travelled to Salisbury
Plain with his son to undertake
a complete survey of the
monument.

Wood presented his findings in
two letters written to the Earl in
the December of 1740. Seven
years later in 1747 these findings
would be published as *Choir
Gaure, Vulgarly called Stonehenge.*

The timing of Wood's
investigation of Stonehenge is
significant, not only was it the
same year that William Stukeley
published his book on
Stonehenge, it was also the
period when *The Origin of
Building* was being prepared for
publication, and Wood was
beginning to compile his *Essay.*
It was a time when his obsession
with Ancient British architecture
was beginning to grow.

E Harris & N Savage, 'John Wood', *British
Architectural Books and Writers 1556-1785,*
Cambridge University Press, Cambridge,
1990, pp.480-489. T Mowl & B Earnshaw,
John Wood: Architect of Obsession, Millstream
Books, Bath, 1988.

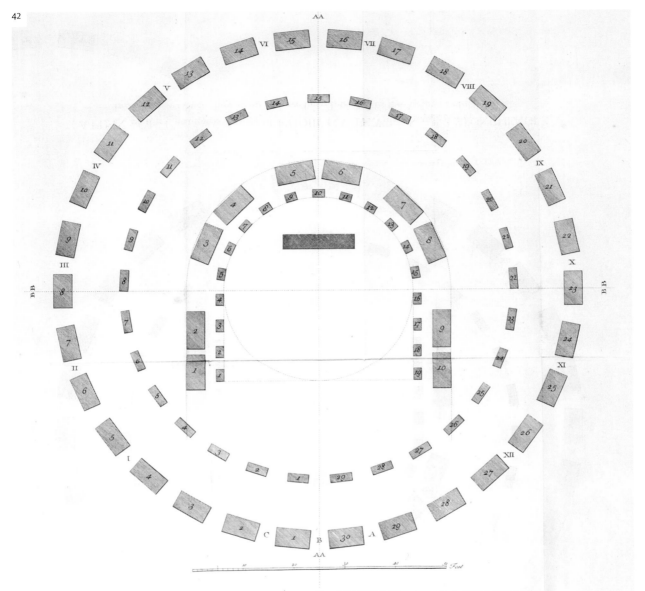

A PLAN of the Contiguous Stones of CHOIR GAURE, Vulgarly called STONEHENGE,
In the perfect State they seem to have been Intended by the Architect of the Work.

102 There has always been, and will always be, a question mark behind Wood's involvement with Freemasonry. The only fact that exists is that there is no written evidence to prove John Wood was a Freemason.

However, at the heart of the art and architecture of Freemasonry is the biblical origin of building, a matter for which Wood attempts to produce evidential proof. But why did he turn to this source for architecture and the orders, instead of the classical theory advocated by Vitruvius and accepted by Wood's contemporary architects? At some point Wood became a part of a group of builders, craftsman, developers and aristocrats who encouraged and promoted the young architect. It was an educated circle, where new ideas must have been discussed and possible lines of investigation proposed. There are other ways by which Wood could have formed relationships with these men, but Freemasonry is the most probable.

Obsession: Freemasonry

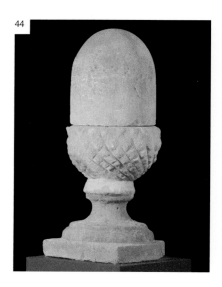

44

43

43 *Bookplate*
Crest of John Wood
c.1740
Printed on paper
98 x 70mm
Bath Central Library, Bath &
North East Somerset Council
B769.52WOO pamph

This coat of arms, which Wood used as a bookplate, illustrates his various obsessions. Interestingly the quarters containing the three crescent moons divided by a chevron are from the heraldry of George Wither, author of *Emblemes*. Also significant is the wild man clutching an oak tree and a club, symbolic of Druidism and Ancient Britain.

T Mowl & B Earnshaw, *John Wood: Architect of Obsession*, Millstream Books, Bath, 1988, pp.200.

44 *Stone Acorns*
Maker unknown
c.1760
Oolitic limestone, Combe Down
Quarry, Bath
940 x 390 x 390mm
Building of Bath Museum
E 0560

The acorns around the parapet of the Circus represent Bladud's discovery of the hot springs of Bath and the druidical history of the monuments the Circus is modelled on. They symbolise John Wood's obsession with Ancient British history

In 1962 these acorns, made of Bath freestone from Ralph Allen's quarries, were removed from the Circus parapet during restoration. They were rescued by the American architect Brown Morton III, who subsequently gave them to an artist friend in Hampstead, London. In 1981 the acorns were moved from Hampstead to South Carolina in America. Earlier this year Mrs Jane Swift generously gave them to the Building of Bath Museum.

There are also visual clues. In 1730 Wood built the Sanctuary of Tyberton Church in Herefordshire, for William Brydges, second cousin of the Duke of Chandos. Inside the Sanctuary, Wood designed an altarpiece made up of carved emblems symbolic of aspects of the Christian Church. The form and use of such emblems on the altarpiece are echoed in the carved metopes of the Doric order in the Circus, many of which depict Masonic devices.

At Tyberton, alongside the instruments of Christ's Passion and the Lamb of God, there is one emblem which does not relate quite so readily to Christian iconography: a sun within a triangle set within a serpent eating its own tail. The serpent is the Ouroborus, the symbol of eternity, the triangle refers to the Holy Trinity, and together they form an emblem of the eternal Trinity.

At the Circus the same three elements are combined in the geometry of the enclosing space. If a line is drawn between the three roads that enter the Circus an equilateral triangle is produced (the Holy Trinity) set within a circle (the symbol of eternity), dedicated to the sun. It is one of the most famous symbols of Freemasonry.

Fig. 59
Left: The Flaming Sun set within the Eternal Trinity, Tyberton Alterpiece, Herefordshire

Fig. 60
Right: The Passion of Christ, Tyberton Alterpiece, Herefordshire

104

On 23 May 1754 John Wood died. He was laid to rest at the church of St Mary the Virgin in Upper Swainswick, the very village where he believed his hero Bladud crashed to his death while attempting to fly off Solsbury hill.

It is possible that the obituary which followed, so full of praise for Wood and censure for his critics, was actually written by the architect himself. However, the best summation of the life and work of John Wood is found in the report of the laying of the Circus foundation stone. It reads like a modern day press release, and was most probably also written by the man himself.

His Buildings, already erected in this City, have been of so great Benefit to this Place in particular, and to the country in general, that while they remain standing Monuments to the World of his Taste in Architecture, they will with grateful Hearts be looked on by our latest Posterity, as the Works of that great Benefactor, and the Name WOOD, the Restorer of Bath, will always be sacred here.

Bath Journal, 18 February 1754

Fig. 61
The tombstone of John Wood the Elder, St Mary the Virgin, Upper Swainswick, Bath

Fig. 62
St Mary the Virgin, Upper Swainswick, Bath

IOANNIS WOOD ARMIGERI

SEPULCHRUM

5. The legacy of John Wood

'Even in the present age Bath is as happily situated for Beautiful works of Architecture as a City can well be.'

John Wood, *An Essay Towards a Description of Bath*

108   The most obvious legacy left by John Wood was the influence he had upon his own son, who completed the Circus and constructed the Royal Crescent. From a very young age John Wood the Younger had been involved in his father's business. Father and son had a strong and mutually beneficial working relationship, but despite inheriting his father's passion for the Palladian style, the younger Wood lacked the qualities that had made his father such a visionary. The son possessed a far greater understanding of the anatomy of a building, but never conceived anything that could match the sheer monumental fantasy of his father's designs.

As the streets laid out by the elder Wood defined the direction of the city's expansion, the method he established of the townhouse terrace was elaborated upon by his son. The next generation of Bath architects emerged and continued to shape the streets and terraces of the city throughout the 18th and into the 19th century.

The influence of John Wood's Bath was far reaching. Heralded by many as the most perfect example of town planning in England, Bath became the model for towns and cities built of squares, circles and crescents. Not long after the younger Wood completed the Crescent in Bath, John Carr would build his own crescent at Buxton in Derbyshire, whilst visitors to Edinburgh cannot fail to recognise the resemblance of the streets of the New Town to those of Bath.

Fig. 63
Royal Crescent, Bath, built by
John Wood the Younger, 1767-74

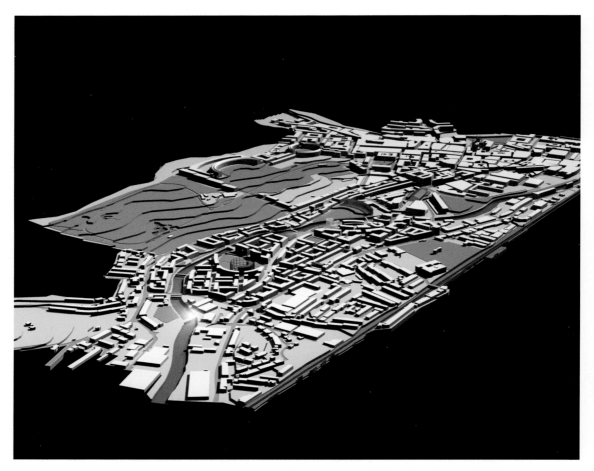

A future vision for Bath

Fig. 64
Opposite, top: possible design solution, Western Riverside, Bath. Grosvenor Estates/ Llewelyn Davies/SWRDA

Fig. 65
Opposite, below left: Transport Interchange proposals, Southgate, Bath. Wilkinson Eyre Architects

Fig. 66
Opposite, below right: Wessex Water, Claverton Down, Bath. Bennetts Associates

Fig. 67
Below left: the restored Hot Bath, Thermae Bath Spa, Grimshaw

Fig. 68
Below right: Proposals for new square, Southgate, Bath. Chapman Taylor Architects

Despite mastering the aesthetic of a Neo-Classical city and forming the epitome of a style to which future architects would aspire, the philosophy behind Georgian Bath failed to find any followers. John Wood was a visionary, but his highly personal and eccentric writings were hard to comprehend. English architects of great vision continued to design monumental and frequently unbuildable structures, but unlike John Wood, very few imagined creating entire cities. Those that did, created extraordinary fantasy designs that remain forever on paper.

250 years after John Wood's death, in an age when the advances in materials and technology are making it increasingly possible to build the unbuildable, less stands between the dreams of visionary architects and their realisation. With many potential sites in Bath waiting to be re-developed, the question is not how do we cope with the inheritance of John Wood's achievements, but rather, when will new architecture emerge that will re-affirm the magnificence John Wood envisaged for the City of Bath?

112 Acknowledgements

The Building of Bath Museum would like to thank the following for their generous support:

Medlock Trust, Heritage Lottery Fund, Aon, Bath Stone Group, Emery's of Bath, Bright Filament Productions Ltd, The Framing Workshop, Jayhawk Ltd, Hamilton Chartered Surveyors, Museum Grants Scheme – administered by Bath & North East Somerset Council, Ken Biggs, Fielden Clegg Bradley Architects, American Museum in Britain, Grosvenor Investments Ltd, Morley Fund Management, Wessex Water, BBC, Moore Stephens, Friends of the Building of Bath Museum, Members of Bath Preservation Trust.

Bev Pound, David Goodey, Professor Dan Cruickshank, Frances Hinchcliffe, Edward Bayntun-Coward, Brown Morton III, Theo Dales, Austyn Bradley, Stephen Morris, David Workman, Tim Spenlove-Brown, Building of Bath Museum Volunteer Guides.

Lenders
University of Bath Library, University of Bristol Library, Bath Central Library, Bath Preservation Trust, Crisp Cowley Chartered Surveyors (Bath), Victoria Art Gallery (Bath), RIBA, Wiltshire Heritage Museum.

Image credits
Fig. 1: Belcomb Brook Villa and garden. Photo: Tim Mowl. **Fig. 2:** Map of Belcomb Brook Villa, Wilts, James Sartain, 1777. Bodleian Library, Oxford; MS. Top. Wilts. c.2 fol. 29. **Fig. 3:** Garden plan of Eastbury, Dorset, Bodleian Library, Oxford: MS. Gough Drawings, a.3 fol.10 (detail). **Fig. 4:** Garden plan for Stowe, Buckinghamshire by Charles Bridgeman c.1720, Bodleian Library, Oxford: MS. Gough Drawings, a.4 f.46. **Fig. 5:** Amphitheatre at Claremont, Surrey. Photo: Tim Mowl. **Fig. 6:** Plan for Amesbury Abbey by Charles Bridgeman, Bodleian Library, Oxford: MS. Gough Drawings, a.3 f.32. **Fig. 7:** The General Plan of Prior Park by John Wood the Elder. *84 Original Architectural Drawings in Somersetshire*, Bath Central Library, Bath and North East Somerset Council. **Fig. 8:** Model of the Royal Forum by Theo Dales. Building of Bath Museum. Photo: Stephen Morris. **Fig. 9:** The Moot, Downton in Wiltshire. Photo Tim Mowl. **Fig. 10/11:** Detail from *The Four Bath Worthies*, Anon, c.1735. Bath Preservation Trust. **Fig. 12:** St Bartholomew's Hospital Archives and Museum. **Fig. 13:** Building of Bath Museum. **Fig. 14:** Ralph Allen's Row, Bath. Photo: Stephen Morris. **Fig. 15:** Dial House, Combe Down, Bath. Photo: Cathryn Spence. **Fig. 16:** Courtauld Institute of Art. **Fig. 17:** Detail, Ralph Allen's Row, Bath. Photo: Stephen Morris. **Fig. 18:** Conduit House, Bowden Hill, Wiltshire. Photo: Francis Kelly. **Fig. 19:** The Royal Mineral Water Hospital, Bath. Photo: Stephen Morris. **Fig. 20:** Garden front of Prior Park, Bath. Photo: Stephen Morris. **Fig. 21:** Plan of the City of Bath, John Wood the Elder, 1735. Bath Preservation Trust. **Fig. 22:** Plan of the Royal Forum, John Wood the Elder, *An Essay Towards a Description of Bath*, Vol III, 1743. Bath Central Library, Bath & North East Somerset Council. **Fig. 23:** Design for a Bridge, John Wood the Elder. Bath Central Library, Bath & North East Somerset Council. **Fig. 24:** Elevation for Buckland House, Berkshire. Bath Central Library, Bath & North East Somerset Council. **Fig. 25:** Elevation for unknown house. Bath Central Library, Bath & North East Somerset Council. **Fig. 26:** Variant elevations for unknown house. Bath Central Library, Bath & North East Somerset Council. **Fig. 27:** Rooftop Pool, Thermae Bath Spa. Nicholas Grimshaw & Partners. Photo: Edmund Sumner. **Fig. 28:** Proposed redevelopment of Southgate, Bath; aerial view from Beechen Cliff. Chapman Taylor Architects. **Fig. 29:** Proposed Transport Interchange, Southgate, Bath. Wilkinson Eyre Architects. **Fig. 30:** Early conceptual design-led approaches to Western Riverside development, Bath. Grosvenor Estates/B&NES/SWRDA. Images: Llewelyn Davies. **Figs. 31/32:** Bath Central Library, Bath & North East Somerset Council. **Figs. 33/34:** University of Bath Library. **Fig. 35:** Special Collections, Information Services, University of Bristol Library. **Fig. 36:** University of Bath Library. **Fig. 37:** Special Collections, Information Services, University of Bristol Library. **Fig. 38:** Llandaff Cathedral Archives. **Fig. 39:** Elevation, Section, Plan of Lilliput Castle, Bath by John Wood the Elder. Bath Central Library, Bath & North East Somerset Council. **Fig. 40:** Belcomb Brook Villa. Photo: Stephen Morris. **Fig. 41:** Elevation of West Front, Titan Barrow Loggia, John Wood the Elder, 1748. Bath Central Library, Bath & North East Somerset Council. **Figs. 42/43/44:** Photo: Stephen Morris. **Figs. 45/46/47:** Bath Preservation Trust. **Figs. 48/49:** Courtauld Institute of Art. **Figs. 50/51:** Photo: Stephen Morris. **Fig. 52:** Bath Central Library, Bath & North East Somerset Council. **Fig. 53:** Photo: Stephen Morris. **Fig. 54:** Bath Central Library, Bath & North East Somerset Council. **Fig. 55:** Manuscripts and Special Collections, University of Nottingham. **Fig. 56:** Trustees of Sir John Soane's Museum. **Figs. 57/58:** Bath Preservation Trust. **Figs. 59/60/61/62/63:** Photo: Stephen Morris. **Fig. 64:** Llewelyn Davies. **Fig. 65:** Wilkinson Eyre Architects. **Fig. 66:** Photo: Peter Cook. **Fig. 67:** Photo: Edmund Sumner. **Fig. 68:** Chapman Taylor Architects.